l⌐ ⌐ners' Resource Cent⌐

⌐4 ⌐NT T⌐l : (014⌐

First Published 1992 by

Casdec Ltd, 22 Harraton Terrace, Birtley,
Chester-le-Street, Co. Durham. DH3 2QG

Tel: (091) 410 5556 Fax: (091) 410 0229

Written by

Rod Corston (BA Hons)

DEDICATED TO:

Mau', Kellie and Lisa

ISBN 0 907595 79 0

RESEARCH METHODS AND STATISTICS IN THE SOCIAL SCIENCES

UNIT 1 - AN INTRODUCTION.

In recent years there has been a massive growth in the demand for courses in the Social Sciences. Whether these courses are 'straight' Psychology or Sociology, or integral parts of Marketing, Management, Nursing or Social Service provisions they inevitably turn at some point, to a consideration of research methods.

For those of us involved in the Social Sciences, research and statistical analysis are an important and inevitable fact of life. Whether or not we are mathematically inclined, we must at some time carry out statistical analysis to enable us to make decisions about the usefulness of our enquiries.

Traditionally, this statistical element of any course has struck fear into the hearts of Social Science students whether at 'A' level or even later, in degree courses. For many, it is without doubt, the sudden re-appearance of 'MATHS' - that bane of long forgotten schooldays which creates this wariness.

Is this fear of statistics inevitable ? - To that question, I would answer an emphatic 'NO' and, I make this statement from the standpoint of one who developed and maintained a fairly impressive aversion to maths at school.

I believe that the traditional teaching of stats. leaves something to be desired. Many Stats. books appear to make what I consider, quite unreasonable assumptions. While I would be the first to agree that they are 'factually perfect', they plough rapidly onwards through reams of text, confident in the belief that all their readers are 'A1 mathematicians'. Simple, 'everyday' examples are rarely offered and the whole topic is rooted firmly in the world of numbers and mathematics. There are few opportunities to draw breath and rarely is any attempt made to ensure that this concentrated reading has actually produced any learning.

You may well ask .... "HOW CAN THIS BOOK BE ANY DIFFERENT"?

Well, it embodies a modular system, based upon the established 'Open Learning' principle. In this system, students work on a 'stand-alone' basis, at home or in a class, studying at their own pace with reference to tutors only when and if they feel the need.

- The book is written as a 'user friendly' package and broken into small, manageable units.

- No pre-suppositions are made regarding the reader's previous knowledge (mathematical or otherwise).

- The reader is allowed to progress through the units with breaks for short 'self tests' on the information delivered to date - the test answers may be found by looking back through the current unit.

- There are a number of longer 'Exercise units', set pieces of work usually involving some written work or calculation, to be completed and returned to a tutor for assessment.

- 'Progress Boxes' are placed at the end of each unit. These enable you keep notes of your progress, plus any points you wish to revise.

- All technical terms are clearly explained in Glossaries throughout the package. The important terms are marked, in the text as 'Keywords'

- At the end of each unit (where appropriate) titles for further suggested reading are shown.

- Reference sections give details of all sources referred to.

- Extracts from statistical tables are included, to be used in association with the statistical exercises offered in the package.

So, as you journey through this package, I hope to lead you through the various research methods, look at their rationale and leading from them and their outcomes, look into the processes of statistical analysis.

And a final note -

When writing any technical text, one is faced with the thorny question of gender issues. Particularly, those raised by the use of generic terms such as 'he' or 'she'. In the writing of this package, a conscious decision was made to avoid the use of that clumsy and distracting term 'he/she'. Thus, in the interests of clarity and consistency the word 'he' will be used throughout. This, I assure you has no undertones of sexism, only a desire for clarity and easy reading.

I wish you luck on your journey and hope you find it rewarding.

Good luck !

Rod Corston
(January 1992)

AN INTRODUCTION TO THE CONVENTIONS USED

THE GLOSSARIES:

Terms which are later explained in the glossary sections (at the end each unit) are marked with a small 'asterix symbol' (*).

So as not to be too obtrusive, these symbols are printed thus ... *

For example, the word Empirical would be marked like this - Empirical*

SELF ASSESSMENT QUESTIONS (SAQ's) :

Within or, at the end of each section there are a number of 'Self Assessment Questions', these are clearly marked as SAQ's with the symbol shown below:

SAQ

The answers to each of the the above SAQ's are to be found in the   preceding unit.

EXERCISE UNITS :

These units are designed to further test the topics explained in the text. The exercises are to completed by you, the student and returned to a tutor for assessment.

These units will be headed with the symbol shown below :-

```
****************************************************
****************************************************
**** ******************** EXERCISE UNIT *********************
****************************************************
****************************************************
```

KEYWORDS :-

Those terms in the text which are deemed to be important, or 'keywords' will be printed in BOLD text. There will of course, be occasions where Glossary Terms are also marked as 'Keywords'.

For Example :- The word **Empirical** is marked in BOLD in this sentence

REFERENCES :

At the end of the package there is a full reference section. These references will show the source of any studies or quotes used within the units, plus any recommended texts. These references will be written in the format approved by the "British Psychological Society". They identify the name(s) of the authors, the date and the title of the publication

For example -

Kohlberg (1981), tells us that a study by Kohlberg was published in one of the Scientific Journals (or a book) in 1981. It will be fully referenced as below :-

Kohlberg, L. (1981) *Essays on Moral Development.* New York: Harper & Row.

This reference tells us that, the title of the book (in italics) was "Essays on Moral development". It was published in 1981 by Harper & Row, a New York Publisher.

Another type of reference :-

Guttman, L. (1950) The third component of scalable attitudes. *International Journal of Opinion and Attitude Research, 4, 285 - 7.*

This refers to a study by Guttman, published in 1950. It appeared in a Journal called "International Journal of Opinion and Attitude Research (in italics). It was in Volume 4 and can be found on pages 285 - 287.

To summarise :-

The title of the book or journal will appear in italics. The volume of the journal will be printed in bold (blacker text). The pages will be identified by their numbers - e.g. 266 - 291.

UNIT 2 - METHODS OF INVESTIGATION

Research in the Social Sciences utilises several methods of investigation and, within this unit we will briefly consider the following :

- The Observation
- The Survey
- The Experiment
- The Correlational Study
- The Case Study

Remember that in all forms of research we are attempting to gather - OBJECTIVE* and EMPIRICAL* data. In all the methods discussed every attempt is made to ensure that no bias or preconceived ideas are allowed to creep in and distort our findings.

Let's now look at each of the above in more detail .....

1. THE OBSERVATIONAL STUDY

A Field or Observational Study is, as the name implies one in which the Subjects of the study are Observed or polled for opinions in a natural setting. Studies carried out in 'natural settings' are often referred to as **ETHNOGRAPHIC** STUDIES.

This is in total contrast to an Experiment (discussed later) in which the setting is contrived, often in a laboratory and where the Experimenter has almost total control over all conditions and factors likely to affect his study.

The Observation attempts to portray the events or lifestyle of the observed group in a way which is as unbiased as possible and is hopefully, a true reflection of the group's way of life as perceived by them (selves).

The Observation seeks to draw no conclusions but usually attempts to 'tell it like it is'. However, later work on the findings of the study may well draw conclusions or develop theories. There are two main types of Observational Study

- **NON - PARTICIPANT OBSERVATION** (Overt*)
- **PARTICIPANT OBSERVATION**   (Covert*)

- **Non - Participant Observation:**

As the title suggests, the Observer remains totally detached from the Subjects of the study and simply observes, from a distance and records or reports their activities. One must note however, that the observed group may frequently be aware of the presence of the observers and no attempts are made by them to conceal their presence.

●   **Participant Observation:**

In this situation the Observer actually joins and to all intents becomes a member of the group under observation. He becomes an inside observer and is usually accepted by the group as a 'bona fide'* member, they being unaware of his true purpose or identity. Usually some 'cover story' is concocted to account for or explain his presence in the group.

The Hidden Observer !

The term 'going native' has often been used in this context - a throwback from the work of anthropologists* working amongst primitive tribes. This method has been used by Sociologists and Psychologists in the U.K. and America to study the activities and structures of street gangs, cults and religious groups.

2.   THE SURVEY

Often utilises questionnaires, interviews or postal surveys, the latter can of course be quite costly. Both of these elicit the opinions of the polled Sample and offer a reasonably efficient method of collating data quickly. It does however have its drawbacks (see recommended reading for a critique). For example - People don't always tell the truth, they may tell us what they think we 'want to hear'. They may tell us things which place them in a good light.

SAQ

●   What is meant by an Ethnographic Study'?

●   What is meant by the term 'going native' ?

3. THE EXPERIMENT

Much of the research in Psychology used the so called 'Method of Introspection'*. A process whereby the researchers, or their assistants acted as Subjects* in the studies. They used their own bodies to assess the effects of certain **stimuli*** and then reported and recorded these observations in minute detail. The method was of course very **subjective*** and was regarded as totally 'non - scientific' by those in the other sciences. The adoption of the 'Experiment', a method long associated with the traditional sciences (e.g. Physics, Chemistry, Biology) was perceived as a landmark on the road to Psychology being accepted as a true science.

An Experiment within the context of a Psychological (or any other scientific study) is essentially a controlled situation within which a HYPOTHESIS*, a prediction of likely outcomes is formulated. The researcher will control or manipulate certain conditions and observe the outcomes of these manipulations and evaluate their effect in the light of the Experimental Hypothesis. This type of study allows the researcher a degree of control over external factors which, in a more natural and inevitably less controlled environment could influence and possibly distort the findings of his work. The Experiment will be discussed more fully in a later course unit.

SAQ

- Give two reasons why the findings of a survey may prove to be less than accurate.

4. THE CORRELATIONAL* STUDY

Another method of study we will consider is, the Correlational Study. A study of this nature is used where an Experiment would be impractical or unethical. For example if we wished to study the effect of cigarette smoking upon peoples' lung tissue. It would be quite unethical to ask Subjects to 'begin' smoking, in order to conduct what could become a 'health endangering study'. We would therefore, resort to studying those who already smoke and over a period of time, seek some CORRELATION (a link or connection) between their smoking and lung and respiratory disorders.

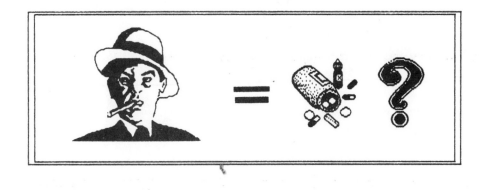

Thus we rely upon the fact that Subjects are already, by choice, experiencing the condition, or experience to be investigated. We may then seek to find some relationship between that **variable** and the observed results.

An extremely important point to note in a Correlational study is that although a Correlation may be found it DOES NOT necessarily suggest CAUSALITY*. We cannot imply cause from an observed Correlation. We must be wary of jumping to the conclusion that when two events are related, or show a correlation) that one actually causes the other.

SAQ

- Why was the adoption of the Experimental method seen as a landmark in the development of Psychology ?

---

5.   THE CASE STUDY

The final method considered is the Case Study, which usually concentrates on only one person. The information is collated* over a period of time and is usually very detailed.   The main drawbacks of this method are :-

- We have only a very limited number of Subjects, albeit studied in great detail

- We often have to rely upon the individual's responses and recollections, theirs and others'. These may be subject to inaccuracies.

- Can we '**generalise**'* from these individual cases, are they typical of the population at large ?

- It is difficult for the researcher who may, of necessity be in the company of the Subject for a great many hours to remain detached and Objective in his observations.

- It may be that the Subject has to recall events which happened many years ago. This recall may be clouded or distorted by many factors

---

SAQ

- If two events are said to be Correlated, would this necessarily mean that one, in some way caused the other ?

- Identify one 'possible' major problem encountered in postal surveys ?

UNIT 2 - METHODS OF INVESTIGATION.

```
************************************************************
************************************************************
********************* EXERCISE UNIT *********************
************************************************************
*********************************************************
```

Please complete the following exercise unit and return your worksheet to your subject tutor

1. A student decides to carry out a participant observation on her own student group. She is interested in the ways her classmates revise for examinations, yet still appear to enjoy their social activities. Discuss how she might carry out this study. Are there likely to be any problems ? If so how may they be avoided or overcome ?

2. You are asked, by a school to carry out an investigation into the play activities of children. The school is specifically interested in the amount of space children use while playing and the levels of aggression shown by some of the children. You decide to carry out an observational study, outline quite how you would go about this :-

   • What will you be looking for and how will you identify and categorise what you see ? It may be useful to devise some 'categories' for this purpose. Explain what you feel would be useful categories.

   • Design some form of record sheet which will be used during the observation period. Draw this sheet and explain how it would be used.

   • Do you anticipate any problems ?

     If so what are they likely to be ?
     If you feel there are likely to be problems, how will you attempt to overcome them ?

GLOSSARY OF TERMS

ANTHROPOLOGIST   -   Literally, one who is involved in the study of mankind, especially the customs and habits of its societies.

BONA FIDE   -   Genuine

CAUSALITY   -   Causality, is the quality shared by two events whereby one is said to have 'caused' the other. e.g. When heat is applied to a kettle of water, the water boils. In this case, the heat is a causal factor in the event of the water boiling.

COLLATED   -   Literally collected, or drawn together

CORRELATION   -   A term used in statistics to imply that two events or variables are in some way related. For example peoples' height and the size of their feet are correlated. As one increases, so does the other.

COVERT   -   Hidden or secret

EMPIRICAL   -   Empirical studies rely upon observation and measurement and not just on theories or ideas.

GENERALISE   -   This is the process whereby an assumption may be made about a whole group or class of people. Often this assumption may be a based solely upon the results obtained from a small section of that group who took part in a study.

HYPOTHESIS   -   Refers to an assumption or prediction made by a researcher before beginning a study. The study then sets out to test the truth (or falsity) of this prediction.

INTROSPECTION   -   The examination of one's own inner thoughts and feelings.

OBJECTIVE   -   Judgements which are objective are said to be free from personal bias or interpretation.

OVERT   -   Open and observable to all, opposite to covert.

GLOSSARY (cont'd)

STIMULI	-	Plural of 'Stimulus'. Any events or actions which stimulate the sense organs.
SUBJECT	-	In the context of scientific investigations, the Subjects are those being studied.
SUBJECTIVE	-	Judgements which are influenced (or coloured) by personal experience, emotion or bias.

SUGGESTED READING

RESEARCH METHODS	-	P. Mc Neill - (1989) Routledge (ISBN 0-415-04126-0)

PROGRESS BOX FOR UNIT 2.

Review the unit and decide, were there any points you feel that you should revise or discuss with your tutor?

Do you understand all of the 'Keywords' ?

Use the box below to record your progress:-

KEYWORDS FOR UNIT 2 :-

OBJECTIVE, EMPIRICAL, ETHNOGRAPHIC,
NON - PARTICIPANT, OBSERVATION, PARTICIPANT
OBSERVATION, ANTHROPOLOGIST, INTROSPECTION, STIMULI,
SUBJECTIVE, HYPOTHESIS, VARIABLE, CAUSALITY

....

Revision Areas :-

....

....

....

....

....

....

....

....

....

....

UNIT 3 - VARIABLES - WHAT ARE THEY ?

When employing research methods in the Social Sciences, you will frequently encounter the term 'variable'. In this unit, we will take a closer look at quite what is meant by that term. For those of you with some experience of algebra or computing, the term may be reasonably familiar. However, let us review quite how we define and identify variables within the context of research in the Social Sciences.

By definition, a variable is 'something which is free to vary' and every day we encounter many variables. The weather, other peoples' behaviour, traffic conditions, our own moods are all variables and as they vary, so they affect the quality of our day. It may be, that we would like to control these so called variables and to some degree, we can.

For example :-

> We may reduce or eliminate the effect of the traffic variable by leaving home earlier and thus avoiding the rush hour.

> We cannot control the weather, but we may, by watching the weather forecasts, minimise the worst of its effects

For the Social Scientist, who is likely to be interested in only one particular **phenomenon***, the variables which surround us in our everyday lives often intrude in his study and distort or confuse results. To overcome this he may attempt to gain some control over these variables and resort to the use of the 'Experiment'.

As explained, the Experiment is essentially a process of beginning with a Hypothesis, or prediction and setting out to test the truth (or falsity) of that prediction. Let's look at an 'imaginary experiment'

We might, for example investigate the unlikely hypothesis, or prediction that :-

> *"People with blue eyes have faster reactions than those with brown eyes".*

To test this hypothesis, we could perhaps gather together two groups of people, one group with blue eyes and one with brown eyes and give both groups the same reaction time test. Ideally, the test should be given, as far as is possible, to people of the same age, at the same times and in the same surroundings etc. as these factors are all variables which may affect the outcome of our study.

We would gather some results in the form of reaction times, we would analyse them and - if the blue eyed group showed faster reaction times. Then we might say, that our hypothesis had been supported, i.e. it had been found to be true. If the brown eyes were faster, we may say the hypothesis had been rejected (i.e. found to be false).

SAQ

- Give a brief explanation of the term Variable

In any Experiment, we attempt to eliminate as many interfering variables as possible and hope to arrive at a situation where only two remain. These two are called the - **INDEPENDENT VARIABLE** (abbreviated to I.V.) and the DEPENDENT VARIABLE (abbreviated to D.V.)

THE INDEPENDENT VARIABLE (I.V.)

In the above study, we can see that there is one fairly obvious variation between the two groups of Subjects. One group has blue eyes and the other brown, we would therefore say that eye colour is the Independent Variable.

This is the variable which we, the Experimenters control. We control it because we have split our research Subjects into two groups, decided by their eye colour. If we find some difference in the reaction times between our two groups, we may reasonably assume that this difference is actually due to the fact that the groups have different eye colours

We may hope that, as far as is practicably possible, this is the only way in which the two groups differ. We have cancelled out, or controlled all the other factors which may affect the Subjects' reaction times. For example - Age, occupation, different surroundings at the time of the test, tests carried out at different times of day, background distractions and any others we may think of.

In short, we attempt to rule out any differences, other than eye colour which may have an effect upon reaction times.

• THE DEPENDENT VARIABLE (D.V.)

Returning to our above study, the second variable, the variation between the Subjects' results, is the Dependent Variable, i.e. the actual reaction times recorded from each group of Subjects. If our hypothesis is correct, then we should find that there is a variation between the two groups. The group with blue eyes should be faster. If this happens, then our hypothesis was correct, if there is no difference then our hypothesis was not correct.

To summarise:-

• In any Experimental situation we hope to eliminate or control all elements or variables which may affect the outcome of our study. To do this, we design the study in such a way as to ensure that the only difference between the two groups being tested is the one, in which we are interested. In the above situation it was eye colour, remember, that was the Independent Variable.

• According to our hypothesis, our Subjects' behaviour, or reaction times will, we hope, be influenced by this difference. Their behaviour is thus dependent upon the difference between the groups. Therefore, their behaviour i.e. their individual reaction time, is the Dependent variable.

• It may help to remember, that in most Experiments, the Dependent Variable will always be the one we measure or record as our Raw Scores*.

SAQ

• Describe what is meant by the term Independent Variable.

• Describe what is meant by the term Dependent Variable.

TYPES OF VARIABLES

When dealing with the 'raw data', collected in our studies we must be aware of the fact that the 'type' of data we collect has some implications for any later analysis we may make.

There are three main types of data :-

- **NOMINAL** (or DISCRETE*)

- **RANK** (or ORDINAL*)

- **CONTINUOUS** (or INTERVAL)

NOMINAL (or DISCRETE) VARIABLES -

These are variables which are "named" and fall into named categories. Each category is quite distinct from the others. These categories are said to be DISCRETE*.

e.g.   Yes   -   No
         Large   -   Small

         Win   -   Lose
         Labour   -   Conservative - Liberal

They belong to one 'named' category and are not transferable to the other.

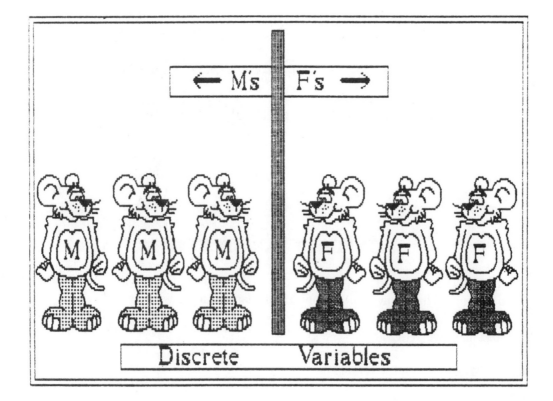

For example, if we devised a study which investigated any differences in recall from short term memory, between males and females . The Independent Variable would be 'sex'. Subjects would clearly fall into one of two categories in this discrete variable, i.e. male or female. Patently they could not belong to both categories nor could they (easily) swap from one to the other.

RANK (or ORDINAL*) VARIABLES -

Variables which are in rank or order e.g. 1st, 2nd, 3rd, 4th etc. each having a place in a hierarchy.

Ranked Variables

This placing only gives us detail in terms of the relative performance of the Subjects. It doesn't tell us how large any of the individual scores were, nor how great the differences were between them.

CONTINUOUS VARIABLES -

These variables are used to represent items which can change in value e.g. times, pressures, weights, heights, speeds and can clearly increase in graduations 1.2, 1.4, 1.6 etc.

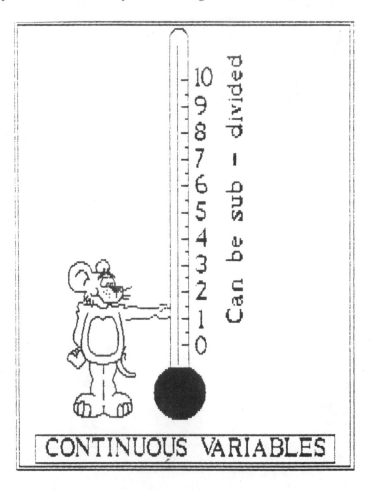

The continuous variables, are much more informative than some of the others and are extremely useful in terms of the information they convey.

> We can see at a glance the scores of each individual
> From this, we could deduce the relative positions of each Subject in the group
> We could convert these scores into discrete variables, i.e. high/low or pass/fail
> We could convert them into rank variables

Therefore, in terms of power of analysis the types are data are ranked in terms of their usefulness as below -

Most useful

1. CONTINUOUS
2. RANK
3. DISCRETE

Least useful

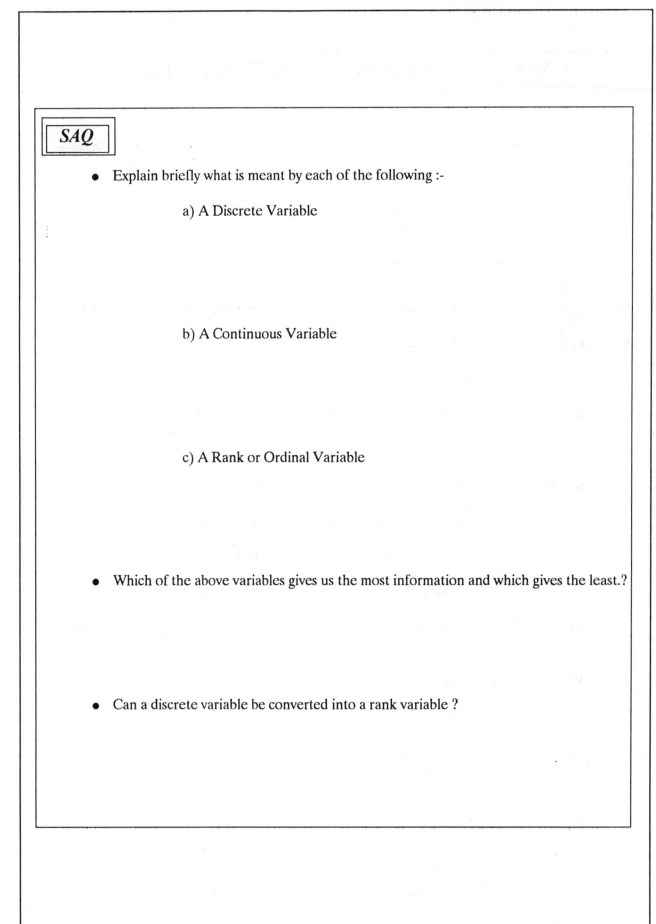

SAQ

- Explain briefly what is meant by each of the following :-

    a) A Discrete Variable

    b) A Continuous Variable

    c) A Rank or Ordinal Variable

- Which of the above variables gives us the most information and which gives the least.?

- Can a discrete variable be converted into a rank variable ?

UNIT 3 - VARIABLES - WHAT ARE THEY ?

```
***************************************************
***************************************************
********************* EXERCISE UNIT *********************
***************************************************
***************************************************
```

Please complete the following exercise unit and return your worksheet to your subject tutor

1. Identify the Independent and the Dependent Variables in the following statements :-

    a) Noise affects fine motor skills.

    b) Children who watch 'soap operas' will have poor reading skills.

    c) Athletes will have faster reactions than non athletes.

    d) Actors will be more extravert (outgoing & sociable) than non actors.

    e) Arts students will be less creative (imaginative) than Science students.

    f) Children whose parents are divorced are more likely to become delinquent.

    g) An audience will have an effect upon Subjects' performance of a task.

    h) Anagrams of common words will be solved more quickly than anagrams of uncommon words.

2. What variable types are described below :-

    a) Temperatures in degrees Fahrenheit

    b) Childrens' ages

    c) The finishing positions in a marathon

    d) The finishing times of the competitors in the above marathon.

    e) The haircolour of the members of your class or group

    f) The time taken for cockroaches to run into a darkened cone.

    g) The categories of behaviours shown by children at play

GLOSSARY OF TERMS

DISCRETE   -   Separate or distinct, each having its own
                                 classification or category.

ORDINAL   -   In order or rank

PHENOMENON   -   Means quite literally an
                                 event which is perceived.

RAW SCORES   -   The actual results recorded during a study.
(RAW DATA)   These may be in the form of scores, times,
                                 temperatures etc.

RECOMMENDED READING

EXPERIMENTAL DESIGN AND STATISTICS IN PSYCHOLOGY - C. Robson
    (1983) -   Penguin books   (ISBN - 0-14-02.2603-6)

PROGRESS BOX FOR UNIT 3.

Review the unit and decide, were there any points you feel that you should revise or discuss with your tutor?

Do you understand all of the 'Keywords' ?

Use the box below to record your progress :-

KEYWORDS FOR UNIT 3 :-

*PHENOMENON, INDEPENDENT VARIABLE, DEPENDENT VARIABLE
RAW SCORES, RAW DATA, ORDINAL DATA, RANK DATA
DISCRETE DATA, NOMINAL DATA, CONTINUOUS DATA*

Revision Areas:-

....

....

....

....

....

....

....

....

....

....

UNIT 4 - THE HYPOTHESIS

Before embarking upon any Experiment, an Hypothesis is formulated. Thus, in an Experiment, we will seek to gain support for, or rejection of the Hypothesis.

There are two different ways in which we can state a Hypothesis :-

- **The Null*** Hypothesis (abbreviated to Ho)

 or

- **The Alternative Hypothesis** (abbreviated to H_1 and sometimes called the Experimental Hypothesis)

To return to a study we discussed earlier in which we investigated the possible effect of eye colour upon Subjects' reaction times.

We could state either :-

THE NULL HYPOTHESIS

Which would predict :-

"There will be no difference in measured reaction times between Subjects with blue eyes and Subjects with brown eyes".

 or

THE ALTERNATIVE HYPOTHESIS

Which would predict :-

"Subjects with blue eyes will have faster measured reaction times than those with brown eyes.

Once we have carried out the Experiment and analysed our data, the results will cause us to do one of two things :-

- If we find that there was a difference in reaction times. We would accept that eye colour does have an effect - In this case we would, reject the Null Hypothesis and accept the Alternative Hypothesis. or

- If there was no difference in reaction times. We would accept that eye colour has no apparent effect - In this case we would, accept the Null Hypothesis and reject the Alternative Hypothesis.

In serious experimental work, the usual procedure is to seek to REJECT the Null Hypothesis.

Why Should this be ?

The difference between the two may appear to be little more than playing with words, but the difference depends upon a quite valid form of reasoning.

If for example we begin with and finally accept the Alternative Hypothesis, then we are saying that "Eye colour does affect Subjects' reaction times." Now, this may well be the case on this particular occasion and in this particular study, but can we be sufficiently certain that this will always be the finding of all future studies.

A much more acceptable statement, would be to say that 'at present', we fail to reject the Null Hypothesis. Now, we are not actually saying that we accept the fact that eye colour affects reaction times, but only that, at this point in time, we have insufficient evidence to reject it as untrue.

Let's look in more detail at quite why we should use the Null Hypothesis at all ?

The reason is actually related to the manner in which we decide whether any differences we find in the performance between our two groups are really 'important' differences, or as they are described in statistical terms - 'Significantly different'. More of the term significant in a later unit.

Let's recap - Before commencing a study, it is customary to express the hypothesis in the Null form. Thus we are actually saying before we begin, that we predict that there will be no differences, i.e. zero difference in the performance of the two groups.

Saying this, forces us to look for any differences which are greater than zero and then measure them.

If the two groups perform in exactly the same way, then their **mean, or** average scores will be identical and we would deduce that there was no measurable difference in their performances. In this case, we would accept the Null Hypothesis.

If however, there is a difference in the mean scores, it would have some value greater than Zero and so suggest that the two groups actually showed different levels of performance. Here, we would reject the Null Hypothesis.

A Question .....

How big, must a difference in mean scores be, to be considered important?

To answer this, we usually resort to the use of statistical tests and then refer the results of our calculations to a set of statistical tables. These tell us whether the differences we have observed are large enough to be considered to have been caused by our Experimental variables. In this case a difference in performance brought about by 'eye colour'.

The greater the recorded difference is away from zero, or 'no difference' the less likely it becomes that this difference (between the two groups' behaviour) has happened by some 'fluke' or chance. We may then deduce that, in our study, the difference in reaction times was due to the fact that one group had blue eyes and the other had brown.

SAQ

- Briefly explain what is meant by an Hypothesis

- How does the Null Hypothesis differ from the Alternative Hypothesis ?

- Why should we attempt to reject the Null Hypothesis ?

- Why have an Hypothesis at all ?

- Why use the Null Hypothesis?

UNIT 4 - THE HYPOTHESIS

```
******************************************************
********************************************************
******************** EXERCISE UNIT ********************
********************************************************
******************************************************
```

When we formulate an hypothesis, we must be sure that it has been 'operationalised. This means that we must define it in terms of what we will measure. There is little point in designing an experiment with the hypothesis :-

Children who watch television will be more delinquent !

What do we mean by watch television, what sort of programmes and for how long? - What do we mean by 'more delinquent - How will we measure delinquency?

Please complete the following exercise unit and return your worksheet to your subject tutor

- Given the following statements, express each as a fully operationalised Alternative Hypothesis with the variables operationalised.

  - Noise affects motor skills.
  - Children who watch television will have poor reading skills.
  - Athletes will have faster reactions than non athletes.
  - Arts students will be less creative (imaginative) than Science students.
  - Children whose parents are divorced are more likely to become delinquent.
  - An audience will have an effect upon Subjects' performance of a task.
  - Anagrams of common words will be solved more quickly than anagrams of uncommon words.

- In your own words, describe the way in which a Null hypothesis differs from the Alternative hypothesis.

GLOSSARY

NULL   -   In this application the word null implies its usual meaning, i.e. nil or none. We thus apply it to the hypothesis which states 'no' difference'

SIGNIFICANT   -   A term used in statistics to signify that an event or result is important. We will meet the term later in the unit where (hopefully) its use will be more easily understood.

RECOMMENDED READING

EXPERIMENT, DESIGN AND STATISTICS IN PSYCHOLOGY

C. Robson (1983) -   Penguin books (ISBN - 0-14-02.2603-6)

PROGRESS BOX FOR UNIT 4

Review the unit and decide, were there any points you feel that you should revise or discuss with your tutor?

Do you understand all of the 'Keywords' ?

Use the box below to record your progress :-

KEYWORDS FOR UNIT 4 :-

*NULL HYPOTHESIS, ALTERNATIVE HYPOTHESIS,
AVERAGE, SIGNIFICANT.*

Revision Areas :-

....

....

....

....

....

....

....

....

....

UNIT 5 - THE EXPERIMENT

Several methods of investigation utilised in the Social Sciences have been discussed earlier and we will now consider the Experimental Method in more detail

All disciplines which set out to investigate scientific phenomena, have a primary concern. That is the acquisition of objective, empirical*, or measurable data. Given this data, analysis may then be carried out and conclusions drawn.

The adoption of the Experiment as a research tool in Psychology, provided an alternative to other, less 'controlled systems' within the field. It allowed Psychology to make a stronger claim to its being a 'Science'. The Experiment was a method already used by some of the older and more accepted Sciences, e.g. Physics, Chemistry and it provided an objective system of inquiry.

A famous psychologist, William James (1890) referred to the Experiment as :-

"The rule of one variable"

The one variable he referred to, was the observable / measurable outcome of the study - i.e. the results or **data*** being measured.

Those who conduct an Experiment, are referred to as Experimenters always written with a capital E and frequently abbreviated to 'E'.

Those taking part in the study, are properly referred to as Subjects, always with a capital S and sometimes abbreviated to 'S'.

In an Experiment the researcher will manipulate certain conditions, or variables mentioned earlier and then observe and measure the outcomes of these manipulations and collect some data, which is later analysed.

Let's summarise :-

An hypothesis is formulated and a study designed to test it. This study is implemented and the results, when obtained, analysed to assess whether or not the hypothesis has been supported or accepted as true.

To recap on the concept of the hypothesis :-

> We might, for example, hypothesise that a brick dropped from a tower will fall to earth more quickly than a feather dropped from the same tower, at the same time. To test this hypothesis, we could carry out an Experiment. We could climb a tower and drop a brick and a feather. We could then observe the outcomes and decide whether or not the hypothesis had been supported, was true or had been rejected, was false)

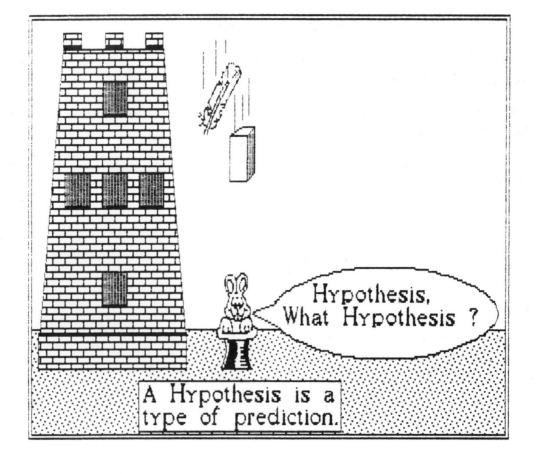

This overall method is called the **Hypothetico - Deductive Method*** and is outlined in the form of a flow chart below :-

THE HYPOTHETICO - DEDUCTIVE METHOD

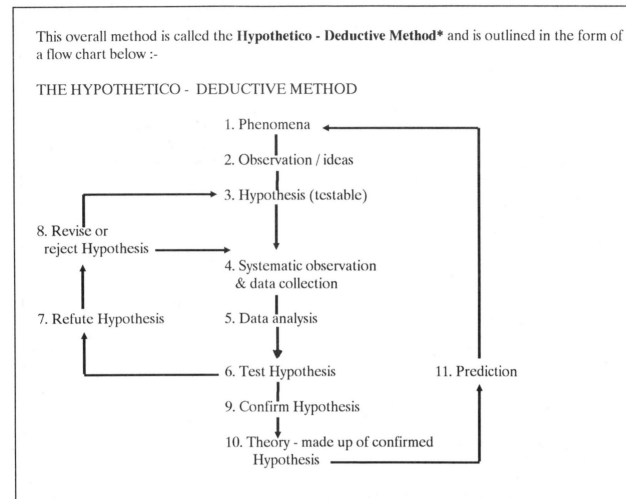

Key to flow chart :-

1. Phenomena exist in the 'real' world and can be observed

2. Scientists actually observe the phenomena

3. An Hypothesis is developed, usually in the form of an intelligent guess, which can be tested, using an experiment.

4. An experiment is carried out and data collected

5. The results (data) are analysed using statistical tests

6. The hypothesis is evaluated in the light of these results

7. The hypothesis is found to be not supported

8. The original Hypothesis is rejected or revised and replaced with a new one

9. If the original Hypothesis is supported

10. This contributes toward a new theory

11. This may be developed into a law, from which further experimental work may be carried out.

Remember, the advantage of the Experimental method is that it allows the researcher some control over external factors which, in a more natural environment could influence and possibly distort the findings of the study.

Returning to the proposition put forward by William James, namely that of the Experiment being 'the rule of one variable'. He refers to the manner in which an Experimenter controls, or manipulates one variable and then observes the outcome of that manipulation upon another variable. Essentially, the process is one of cause and effect. The controlled variable is the 'cause' and the observed variable, or outcome is the 'effect'.

Remember, these variables have specific names:-

THE INDEPENDENT VARIABLE

The variable which we (the Experimenters) usually control and manipulate, then investigate any observable effects or changes upon ....

THE DEPENDENT VARIABLE

This is the 'measured variable' where we may expect to find some changes as a result of our manipulations of the Independent Variable.

To clarify the identity of these two variables let's look at another hypothetical 'Experimental situation' :-

Let us imagine we wish to investigate the effect of alcohol upon driving skills :-

One method might be to observe drinkers' antics as they attempt to drive home after an evening at the 'local' and measure the effects of 'drink' as a function of the number of accidents they cause or are involved in. However, ethical considerations aside, this would be a particularly inefficient method of gaining data.

We would have no **a priori*** measures of :-

- The actual quantity, or type of drinks consumed by the drivers.
- The period over which any drink was consumed.
- The individual drivers' level of driving skill when sober.
- The drivers' physical condition before drinking (tired, ill, drunk already, taking medication).
- Whether or not the drivers' alcohol level was the sole contributory factor to any accidents we observed.

(contd.)

Factors which may affect the individual driver's reaction to alcohol

- Individual's metabolic* rate
- Quantity of food if any consumed during or before drinking
- Habitual intake of alcohol (this affects tolerance)
- Mood or emotional state
- Speed of alcoholic intake

Additionally, we have no quantitative means of measuring the outcomes of the drivers' actions :-

- How would we objectively 'measure' the seriousness of any accidents ?
- How would we evaluate the role played by alcohol, as opposed to any other factors as a cause of this accident ?

In short, these and doubtless many other factors would make it very difficult to measure the effect of alcohol consumption, in this rather haphazard and unscientific way. There are so many "loose ends" in such a study that it could not possibly withstand any serious scrutiny of its findings.

SAQ

- When William James referred to the "rule of one variable", to which variable did he refer?

To establish control and thus greater credibility, we could arrange an Experimental situation and thus ensure the following

- All drivers would be tested sober, in the same car, on an enclosed driving circuit to measure their skill at negotiating a marked course consisting of traffic cones. Skill (The Dependent Variable) being measured as the number of cones knocked over.

- Having established a **norm*** for sober driving skills for each driver we would then ask each to drink a known measure of alcohol, which would in this case be The Independent Variable. They would then attempt to negotiate the course again.

See a diagram of this situation shown overleaf .....

AN EXPERIMENT TO ESTABLISH THE EFFECT
OF ALCOHOL UPON DRIVING SKILLS

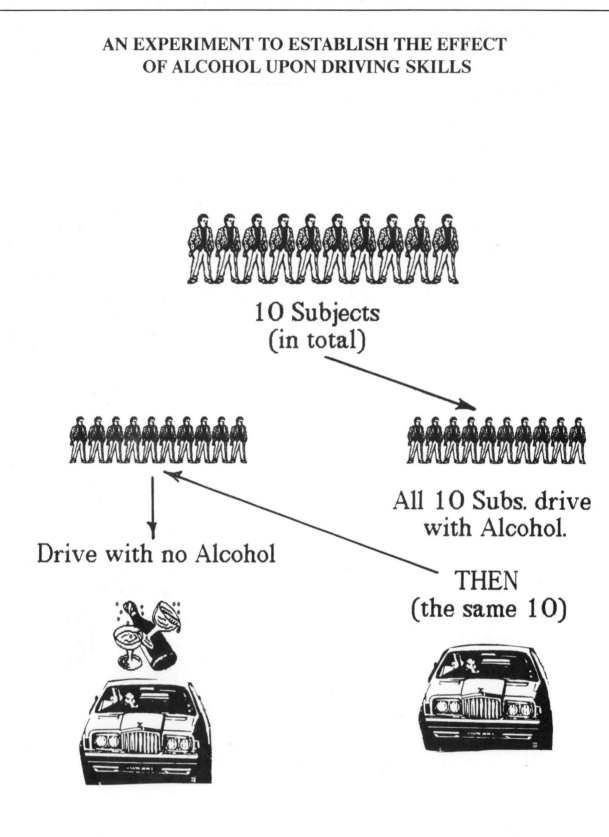

10 Subjects
(in total)

All 10 Subs. drive
with Alcohol.

Drive with no Alcohol

THEN
(the same 10)

However, this is only one method of carrying out this study. An alternative method is shown overleaf.

In this case we might have ...

One group of drivers observed driving the course sober and then record the number of cones they knock down. Then have a different group drive the same course after a measured intake of alcohol and record the number of cones they disturb. A score, based upon the mean (average) number of cones knocked over by each group would be recorded and the results analysed.

10 Subjects

Half of the group drive with Alcohol

Half of the group drive with no Alcohol

It is worth noting that there are advantages and disadvantages in both of the above methods of testing, each represents a specific type of design of Experiment. These designs will be discussed later, along with their implications for the outcomes of the Experiment.

However, to return to our 'alcohol & driving' Experiment. We may adopt some measures to minimise or remove many of the unwanted factors or variables discussed earlier.

These unwanted or extraneous* variables are referred to as SITUATIONAL and MOTIVATIONAL VARIABLES, each having an effect by virtue of :-

- The Experiment's situation.

  or

- The Subjects' motivation.

Although every attempt is made to reduce the incidence of these variables, it is very difficult to exclude all such, potentially disruptive effects.

Various methods and techniques are employed to reduce such extraneous variables to an acceptable level and these will be discussed in a later unit.

SAQ

- What advantages and disadvantages does the Experimental method offer when compared to other types of study ?

- What is meant by the term Extraneous Variables ?

- What is a Situational Variable ?

- What is a Motivational Variable ?

CRITICISM OF THE EXPERIMENTAL METHOD

Although having many benefits and being widely used in the Social Sciences, the Experimental method has often attracted criticism for factors which, arguably are inevitably present in its process. The following are examples of some of these criticisms:-

Dehumanisation :

It may be argued that any Experiment which sets out to examine human behaviour, reduces the Subjects to a level of performers in a very contrived situation. The behaviours they exhibit may be considered, at best untypical and at worst unnatural. It has been claimed by one researcher to offer -

"..... A Mechanistic View of Man"   (Heather 1976).

Against this it may be argued that the controlled environment of the Experiment allows the researcher to gain -

".... A detached, objective and impersonal view of Man"   (Broadbent 1973)

Distortion of Behaviour :

The contrived Experimental situation, produces behaviour which gives a misleading impression of how people behave in real life.

Expectancy Effects :

Are found when a Subject performs in a manner he feels will either please the Experimenter or enhance his own performance.

Swingle (1973) argued that :-

"...... An individual may act in a way he thinks the Experimenter wants him to act, or in a way he feels normal people should act, but not in the way he would behave were he unaware that his behaviour was being observed"

To illustrate this point Orne (1962) asked Subjects to perform a series of extremely pointless and boring tasks. One task was adding together 224 pairs of numbers and then immediately tearing up the answer sheets, before embarking upon the next 224 pairs. He found, that if people believed it was part of an Experiment they would eagerly comply and work quite happily, often for four or five hours at a time, until told by the Experimenter to stop. Had they been simply asked to do this task outside the 'Experimental situation', it is likely that they would have simply refused, or lost interest very quickly.

Another criticism of the Experiment is its **Validity*** as a means of telling us about the performance or behaviour of humans, (in general) based upon the data gathered from the performance of a few.

VALIDITY

External Validity :

Refers to the generalisability of the results of the study out to the world in general. For example, if our study was set in a laboratory and used 20 College students and produced a specific result. Could we then generalise this out to :-

- All students, the world over?
- All people, the world over?

In theory, if the sample of Subjects we have selected is truly 'representative' of the population, then we could feel free to do this. However, if we fail to ensure that the sample is truly representative of the population at large, then we threaten external validity, and generalise in an inappropriate manner (more on 'representative samples later')

GENERALISATION OF THE EXPERIMENT'S FINDINGS

Suppose, that at the end of an Experiment, we achieve a statistically significant result. From this we may suppose, that our manipulation of the Independent variable did indeed have a real effect upon the Dependent variable. Can we now assume that this effect is one which we can generalise out to 'all of the population'. Don't forget, our study only looked at this effect upon a (usually small) 'select' sample.

Let's look at an example :

If we were to use a sample which comprised only nurses and found that an 18 second delay prevented accurate recall of a list of words. Could we generalise the implications of this result out to the population at large? Or, could it be that there is something 'special' about this very select sample. Maybe, nurses are different in some way from the rest of the population, in the way they memorise information.

Some criticism has been levelled at the fact that, most Psychological research uses first year undergraduates, usually Psychology undergraduates for its studies. It seems reasonable to say that they are, just by being at University a very select sample. They are mostly, white and middle class (more so in the States). Can the findings of studies using them be 'safely' generalised out?

Some studies use volunteers. The work of ORA (1965) has shown that there are quite distinct differences between volunteers and the population at large. They are :-

- Abnormally insecure
- Dependent upon and influenced by others
- Aggressive
- Neurotic*
- Introverted*

We should therefore, only generalise our results from studies using these types only, to others of that 'type'.

Many Experiments utilise laboratory rats and again we must be careful about generalising the results of these animal studies, to the population of humans at large.

Internal Validity :

This refers to the certainty we may have, that the I.V. actually produced the effect shown in the D.V.

If this effect has been achieved solely by the manipulation of the I.V., then internal validity has been achieved. Can we always be 'really' sure that this was the case?

SAQ

What do you think Heather (1976) meant when he suggested that the Experiment offered a "Mechanistic view of man" ?

- What is meant by the term 'Expectancy effects' ?

- What is meant by the Generalisation of an experiment's findings ?

- What is External Validity ?

- Why may the use of volunteers as Subjects present a researcher with problems ?

- What is Internal Validity ?

UNIT 5 - THE EXPERIMENT.

```
***********************************************************
***********************************************************
********************* EXERCISE UNIT *********************
***********************************************************
***********************************************************
```

Please complete the following exercise unit and return your worksheet to your subject tutor

1.   Suppose a Psychologist designs an Experiment to test an experimental hypothesis that people will take less time to read a text with illustrations, than the same text without illustrations.

     a)   What is the Independent Variable?

     b)   What is the Dependent Variable?

     c)   What is the predicted relationship between the I.V. and the D.V.?

     d)   What is the Null Hypothesis?

     e)   In your opinion, are there any extraneous variables which should be controlled.?

2.   As sample size increases can we be more or less certain of our experimental results ?

3.   Give reasons why the experiment may be criticised as a research method.

4.   You are asked by a manufacturer to investigate whether or not fluorescent lighting is having an adverse effect upon the workers in his factory. This adverse effect is shown in reduced production rates. Devise and describe an experiment which may investigate this. State the hypothesis, I.V., D.V. and any variables you feel you should control

GLOSSARY OF TERMS

A PRIORI	-	Assumptions based upon previously obtained knowledge.
DATA	-	Usually, the results obtained from a study.
EMPIRICAL	-	Based upon observation and not just on theory or ideas.
EXTRANEOUS	-	Of external origin
HYPOTHESIS	-	The prediction used as a basis for a study. Importantly, no assumptions are made as to the truth or falsity of this hypothesis before commencing the study.
INTROVERTED	-	From Introvert. A term used by C. Jung to describe a personality type. Literally means 'turning inward' and suggests one who is shy, withdrawn etc.
METABOLIC	-	The process by which living cells absorbs nutritional material.
NEUROTIC	-	One who suffers from a neurosis. A form of mental disturbance not due to any apparent physical cause. E.g. depression.
NORM	-	A standard or reference point.
QUANTITATIVE	-	Measured or measurable.
VALIDITY	-	We may say that if something is 'valid', then it is true.

RECOMMENDED READING

RESEARCH METHODS - P. Mc Neill

PROGRESS BOX FOR UNIT 5.

Review the unit and decide, were there any points you feel that you should revise or discuss with your tutor?

Do you understand all of the 'Keywords' ?

Use the box below to record your progress :-

KEYWORDS FOR UNIT 5 :-

DATA, HYPOTHETICO DEDUCTIVE, A PRIORI,
EXTRANEOUS, MOTIVATIONAL, VALIDITY, NORM

Revision Areas :-

....

....

....

....

....

....

....

....

....

....

UNIT 6 - SAMPLING TECHNIQUES & SELECTION OF SUBJECTS

Experimental groups consist of Subjects who have in some way been chosen to take part in an Experiment. The manner in which they are chosen is of great importance to the successful conduct of that experiment. This chosen group is referred to as a **SAMPLE***.

In any Experimental situation, every attempt is made to select a group of Subjects who are, as far as possible, **representative** of the **population*** from which they are drawn or selected. By 'representative, we mean that we hope the methods we have used for selection, have ensured that these Subjects 'perform' no differently to any others we could have chosen from the larger (parent) population.

How do we cut out a 'Representative Sample' ?

This is vitally important because, when we make some statement about the behaviour of the people in our Experimental Sample, we would usually hope to later **generalise*** or extrapolate* to 'all' of the parent population. To do so, we must be certain that our sampled group is as representative as possible of the parent population.

Let's just clarify this. Imagine you have been asked to carry out some market research for a large sports goods retailer. They intend opening a branch in your town and before doing so, they want to ensure that the venture will be worthwhile (profitable). You have been asked to carry out a survey. Suppose you confined your enquiries to one of the older, more run down areas of town.

Do you think the results of your enquiries would be 'representative' of the town at large. ?

If not, then why not ????

When we begin our process of selection for our Sample, we should ensure that the process of selection should allow, insofar as is possible, that every person in the parent population has an equal chance of being chosen within this sample group.

SYSTEMS OF SAMPLING

Let's look at some possible systems of sampling :-

- A possible system of selection could be, to select the names of Subjects from a telephone directory.

  Would this be a good system ?

- We could select Subjects from the platform of a railway station. However, this would effectively debar all those for whom rail travel is too expensive and as a result provide a Sample who share a relatively similar **Socio - Economic*** background reflected in the fact that they can all afford to travel by train.

- We could use the Electoral Register. This lists the names and addresses of all registered voters in a given area. However, if we chose names in the order they appear, we would select people who were, neighbours, living in a similar area, probably of a very similar socio - economic status. Additionally, people who are in prison, or are homeless would not figure in this sample.

All of these factors could contribute to give us a sample which consists of people who are very 'similar', yet very 'different' (as a group) from those living in other areas of the town.

Accepting the above points as valid, how can we ever hope to achieve anything approaching a truly representative or **'Random Sample**

Well, there are several methods available to us in our role as a researchers :-

● **Systematic Sampling :**

If for example a sample of 100 was to be drawn from a population of 2000.   A systematic technique would select, say every 20th person.   The actual starting point of the selection process would be chosen at random.

● **Stratified Sampling :**

This involves dividing the population into **homogenous*** groups - e.g. Males and Females and then sampling from each of the different groupings

● **Cluster Sampling :**

If the target population is widely dispersed, sampling becomes difficult and expensive, in view of the time and travel involved.

In this case the researcher would decide upon a grouping system, within the total population and then select random samples from within each groupings.

● **Opportunity Sample :**

Subjects selected on a random basis from those available at the time.   e.g. fellow students, friends, work colleagues.   This is probably the commonest system used in College or school courses.

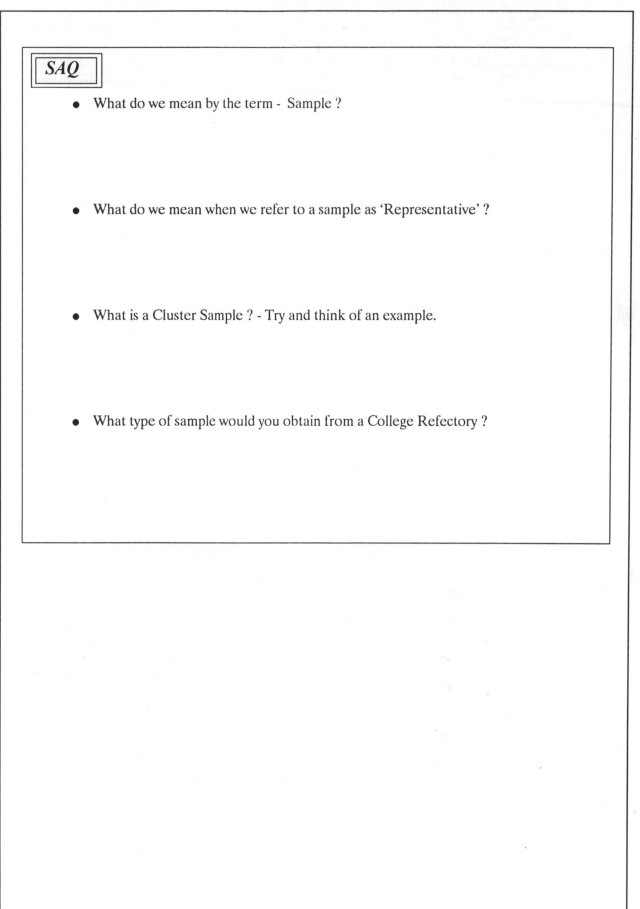

SAQ

- What do we mean by the term - Sample ?

- What do we mean when we refer to a sample as 'Representative' ?

- What is a Cluster Sample ? - Try and think of an example.

- What type of sample would you obtain from a College Refectory ?

UNIT 6 - SAMPLING TECHNIQUES

```
****************************************************
******************************************************
******************** EXERCISE UNIT ********************
******************************************************
****************************************************
```

Please complete the following exercise unit and return your worksheet to your subject tutor

1. Is a sample chosen from the Saturday morning customers at British Home Stores a representative sample of 'general shoppers'?

2. A researcher is interested in the different child rearing styles of working class and middle class mothers. One group will be selected from a 'middle class area' and one from a 'working class area'. What care should be taken when selecting the study sample to ensure the two groups are truly comparable ?

3. Suggest three methods by which the total sample selected for a study could be 'randomly' divided into two groups.

4. A psychologist asked for volunteers who lived in the North East of England to take part in a study. She was testing the hypothesis that there would be a relationship between drinking alcohol and unemployment. After the results were analysed, it became apparent that there was indeed a positive correlation between the two. A statement was then issued to the effect that, there was a relationship between levels of unemployment and consumption of alcohol. From this, some people decided that 'drinking alcohol' leads to unemployment. Given the results of the study, was that a reasonable supposition - explain your answer?

GLOSSARY OF TERMS

EXTRAPOLATE - Estimate from known data or information.

GENERALISE - If we generalise from our data, then we make the prediction that because all of our Subjects performed in a certain manner, then all Subjects (in general) must perform the same way.

HOMOGENOUS - Of the same or very similar kind.

POPULATION - The major group upon whom the study is being carried out. From this large group, we select our sample.

SAMPLE - A small group drawn from the population. This group is then viewed as being (as far as possible) representative, of all others in the population,

SOCIO - ECONOMIC - Relating to social position and economic status.

RECOMMENDED READING

RESEARCH METHODS - P. Mc Neill.

PROGRESS BOX FOR UNIT 6

Review the unit and decide, were there any points you feel that you should revise or discuss with your tutor?

Do you understand all of the 'Keywords' ?

Use the box below to record your progress :-

KEYWORDS FOR UNIT 6 :-

REPRESENTATIVE SAMPLE, EXTRAPOLATE, HOMOGENOUS SOCIO - ECONOMIC, RANDOM SAMPLE, OPPORTUNITY SAMPLE, CLUSTER SAMPLE, STRATIFIED SAMPLE, GENERALISE.

Revision Areas :-

....

....

....

....

....

....

....

....

....

UNIT 7 - CONTROLLING EXTERNAL VARIABLES

In any study, researchers must be aware of factors, other than those which are 'intentionally' manipulated within their work which may influence, or distort their findings. These factors are called, Extraneous or Confounding variables. They are perceived as being **extraneous** or external to the study and thus may well confound, or distort the results.

An example of some extraneous variables may be seen in the following example :-

> An Experimenter decided to investigate the effect of caffeine* upon stress. He selected for his research, a group of coffee drinking colleagues all of whom lectured at the same University. The period of the study was the five week Xmas vacation.

> He randomly divided the group into halves. One group was told to drink only decaffeinated coffee, the other drank their usual brands. At the end of the vacation, all of the 'decaffeinated group' reported, via a questionnaire that they felt less stressed. When all Subjects were checked for physiological symptoms of stress, it was found, that the 'decaffeinated group' did indeed show a lower levels of stress.

The above study is an example of poor design and is simply 'bursting' with confounding variables - For example :-

● Although the stress levels did fall, for the decaffeinated group, we may assume it could also fall for the other group, who must surely be less stressed while on holiday. Thus there is one element of stress reduction in place already.

- The effects of no caffeine, plus the effects of the vacation may be very different from the effect of caffeine reduction alone. How do we separate the effects of the vacation from the supposed effects of reduced caffeine levels?

- Some Subjects may derive greater benefits, in terms of stress reduction from vacations than others. If the Experimenter had been particularly unlucky, he could have unwittingly allocated all those who show greater vacation stress reduction to the no caffeine group. His results would then wrongly show caffeine reduction, as a means of reducing stress.

- Did he check levels of stress in all Subjects, before he began the study?

- Can we be sure that all of the Subjects ate and drank in a similar manner during the vacation? This may affect stress. Can we be sure of the effects of alcohol and caffeine intake, in relation to stress? Could the Xmas situation and its fare contribute differently to each individual's stress levels?

- The Experimenter himself may have been biased when he examined his Subjects for stress. If he proposed that caffeine 'causes' stress, he may well display Experimenter Bias and actually look harder, for signs of stress in one group than he does in the other.

The above described extraneous variables actually divide into two types :-

- **SITUATIONAL**

    Insofar as they are created by the 'situations' the Subjects are placed in i.e. the vacation, the Xmas experience, their surroundings during the vacation etc.

- **MOTIVATIONAL**

    Factors affected by the individuals' **attributes***, their age, personality, mood, drinking / eating habits etc.

The following section outlines some of the major, recognised extraneous or confounding variables :-

SITUATIONAL VARIABLES

THE EXPERIMENTAL EFFECT :-

This is induced by the Experimental situation itself. Sometimes called the Hawthorne effect. This refers to a study carried out in 1927 by MAYO and is simply due to the fact that an Experiment is taking place.

Mayo's study was intended to investigate the relationship between working conditions, workers' levels of tiredness and levels of production. The study was carried out in a factory producing telephone relays.

A test area was set up and the employees, 5 female volunteers working in the area, knew that the study was taking place and that they were the Subjects

Mayo varied working conditions, temperature, humidity levels, rest breaks, and length of working day and to his surprise, he found that regardless of what changes he made, output went up consistently.

The reasons, after much investigation were found to be that the girls had formed a strong group identity and worked hard, simply to please the Experimenters. Thus it provided a situation, where the Experimental setup itself, had created the improvements and not the various measures being introduced.

THE EXPERIMENTER EFFECT :-

This effect owes less to the Experiment and more to the behaviour and attitudes of the 'Experimenter' himself. The effect may become apparent where an Experimenter unwittingly influences the behaviour or responses of Subjects as a result of his own beliefs or expectations. For example if he expects a certain outcome to the Experiment he may unwittingly offer encouragement to produce this outcome and thus introduce some covert* positive reinforcement*.

Experimenters can rarely be viewed as disinterested third parties. They obviously have a vested interest in the area of their study and arguably, some 'expectations'. If not, they would not be carrying out the Experiment.

LYONS (1964) Said :-

> The Experimenter wants Subjects to be perfect servants - intelligent individuals who will cooperate and maintain their position without becoming hostile or negative.

It is easy to see why such a desire exists.

The area of Experimenter effects may be further broken down :-

● Experimenter **attributes*** :

These are the attributes of the Experimenter himself:-

> Biosocial* attributes, may include age, sex, race and religion and the values associated with these factors.

> Psychosocial* attributes may include, anxiety level, need for social approval, hostility, authoritarianism*, intelligence and dominance.

Situational Factors - whether or not the Subs and Experimenter have had previous contact, e.g. - Is Experimenter experienced. - Is Subject friendly, hostile or perhaps nervous.

- Experimenter Expectancies

    Bias due to the Experimenter's expectations in terms of the outcome of the Experiment. There is strong evidence to show that in some studies, the Experimenters have actually recorded responses 'inaccurately' in a manner which best supports their expectancies.

This may be overcome by :

- The use of **standardised printed or taped instructions to Subjects,** which relieve the Experimenter of the need to talk to Subjects. This also ensures that everyone receives exactly the same instructions.

- The use of the "DOUBLE BLIND". In this situation the Experimenter will, himself be unaware of the "condition" the Subject is currently   experiencing. For example, if the Experiment was to investigate the effect of a drug upon reaction time and a control or placebo* drug was being used to ensure equal treatment for each group of Subs. The Experimenter, or assistant would be kept in ignorance as to which drug was being administered, to which group at any given time.

SAQ

- Give three examples of :- Situational variables

MOTIVATIONAL & SUBJECT EFFECTS

MOTIVATIONAL EFFECTS

Any Subject involved in an Experimental situation, of any sort will inevitably experience 'different' feelings from those found in more natural settings.

At a minimal level he will feel :-

- Apprehensive
- Observed
- Extra cooperative
- Highly sensitive to the surroundings
- Suspicious
- Alert
- Self conscious
- Apprehensive at the prospect of being 'tested' (Evaluation Anxiety)

Positive Self Presentation :

Refers to the need Subs feel to show themselves in the best possible light. They will attempt to behave in the manner they feel will, in the light of their perceptions of what is required show them to be most effective and positive.

Subject Sophistication :

Refers to the way in which Subjects may themselves be familiar with the methods of Psychology and Experimentation. This can be avoided by the use of naive volunteers or subs. However it is as well to note that most studies, here and in the US, actually use Psychology Undergraduates in their studies. Surely an example of a very sophisticated or non - naive* sample.

MOTIVATIONAL VARIABLES

These variables are very much dependent upon the Subjects' own physical / psychological state and may be the result of

Tiredness -

To avoid this, we could arrange for all Subs. to be tested at same time of day and ensure that all are equally alert or equally tired.

Fatigue or Boredom -

Avoided by attempting to ensure some variety in delivery of the Experimental material or, ensure all Subjects are "equally bored".

Practice effects -

This occurs when Subjects perform two tasks, let's say Task A then Task B. It may be that the processes involved in performing Task A, actually give the Subs. some advantage when they later come to perform task B.

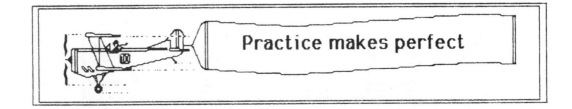

Practice makes perfect

OTHER METHODS OF CONTROL

Some other methods of Control may be introduced by virtue of the manner in which the Experiment is conducted

RANDOMIZATION :

This usually refers to the manner in which Subjects are assigned to Experimental groups.

The initial selection process should be, as random as practicably possible and then the allocation of these Subjects to their respective groups should be further made on a random basis. For example, toss a coin, draw names from a hat, use a computer to generate random numbers or use random number tables.

COUNTERBALANCING :

This avoids the effect of order, carry over or practice effects. It involves the alternate ordering of conditions.

e.g.   If a study required Subjects to carry out two tasks, Task A and Task B.

We might have the first Subjects carry out Task A first, followed by Task B. The next Subject would carry out B then A, the next A then B and so on.

This is a method of reducing effects which cannot otherwise be practically eliminated from the Experiment. The procedure accepts that inevitably, some factors cannot be removed from the scene. It simply attempts to reduce or eliminate unwanted effects of practice for all Subjects.

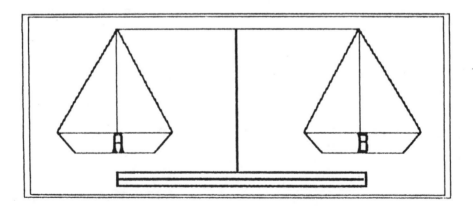

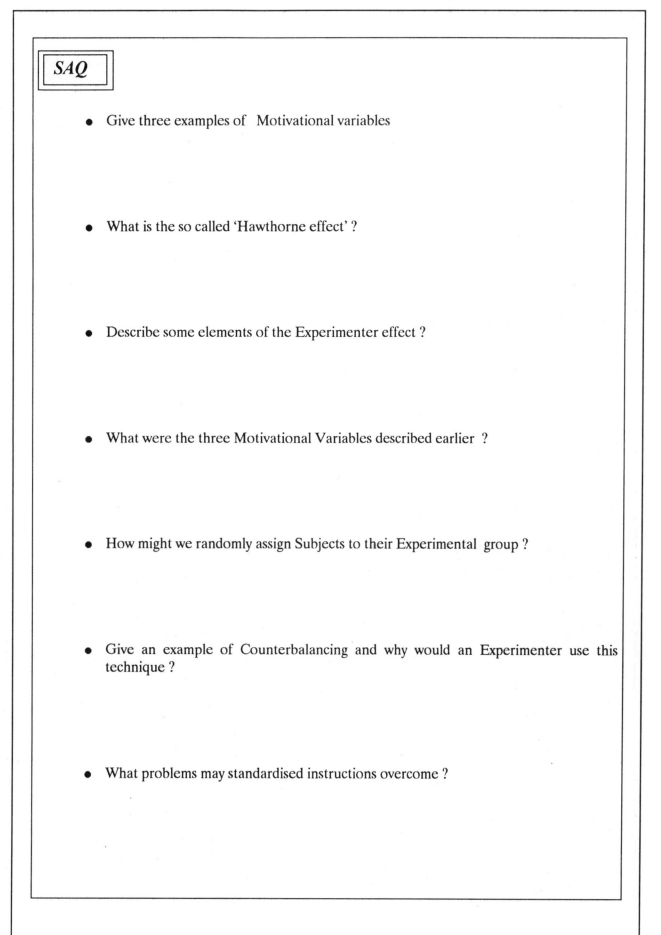

SAQ

- Give three examples of Motivational variables

- What is the so called 'Hawthorne effect' ?

- Describe some elements of the Experimenter effect ?

- What were the three Motivational Variables described earlier ?

- How might we randomly assign Subjects to their Experimental group ?

- Give an example of Counterbalancing and why would an Experimenter use this technique ?

- What problems may standardised instructions overcome ?

THE CONTROL GROUP

In many experiments, the researcher may wish to use a '**Control Group**'. This is a group which is not exposed to the test conditions of the actual Experiment. It provides a group, which can be used by the researcher as a base line or reference from which to compare the results of his Experiment.

For example, if we wished to examine the effectiveness of two different teaching systems, each designed to teach primary school children to spell (system A and System B).

We could have one group of children use system A, the other group use system B and then carry out our study over a period of one year. During the year, we could give spelling tests at regular intervals to evaluate progress. At the end of the year, we would analyse the results and decide which system was the more effective.

From this we will certainly know how children perform with system A and with system B. However, what we don't know, is how well the children would have progressed had they used neither system and simply remained on their current or traditional system'

How could we overcome this ? Well, we would simply introduce a Control group as shown in the diagram below :-

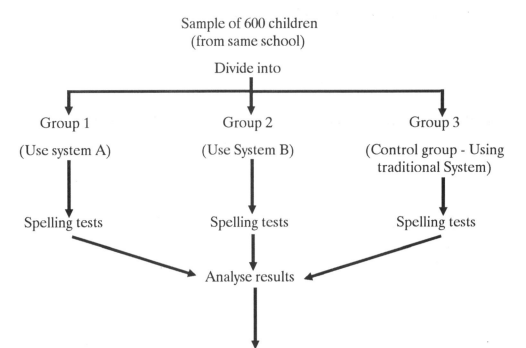

The Control group would be taught using the usual system. They would have traditional teaching methods and the regular spelling tests. This would separate any improvements in the childrens' spelling, in this group which occur simply as a result of the passage of time or, from the use of the traditional system at the school.

SAQ

- Imagine that you have been employed by a drug company to test a new cold cure. Briefly describe how you would design a study to test the effectiveness of the new drug.

  Would you use a control group and if so How ???

GLOSSARY OF TERMS

ATTRIBUTES   -   The fundamental qualities of a person or stimulus

CAFFEINE   -   A stimulant found in tea and coffee.

COVERT   -   Hidden or concealed.

NAIVE   -   Innocent. In the case of an experiment, a naive Subject would be one who had no idea as to the true purpose of the study.

PLACEBO   -   A substance with no medicinal value, which when administered, provides apparent relief.

POSITIVE REINFORCEMENT   -   In simple terms a positive reinforcer is one which is perceived as rewarding.

RECOMMENDED READING.

AN INTRODUCTION TO EXPERIMENTAL DESIGN
IN PSYCHOLOGY - A CASE APPROACH

H. H. Johnson & R. L. Solso (1978) - Harper & Row (ISBN - 0-06-043413-9)

PROGRESS BOX FOR UNIT 7

Review the unit and decide, were there any points you feel that you should revise or discuss with your tutor?

Do you understand all of the 'Keywords' ?

Use the box below to record your progress :-

KEYWORDS FOR UNIT 7 :-

*COVERT, ATTRIBUTES, BIOSOCIAL, PSYCHOSOCIAL
STANDARDISED INSTRUCTIONS, DOUBLE BLIND, PLACEBO
RANDOMIZATION, COUNTERBALANCING, CONTROL GROUP.*

Revision Areas :-

....

....

....

....

....

....

....

....

....

....

UNIT 8 - EXPERIMENTAL DESIGN

Having selected our sample, we must now decide upon a design for our study. If you recall, in our 'drink and driving study', we proposed two possible alternatives :-

a)   Have the same group of drivers take part in two driving tests. One trial 'drunk' and the other 'sober'.

or

b)   Have two different groups of drivers. One group drives 'drunk' and the other drives 'sober'.

These two designs, plus one other, comprise the three Experimental designs we will consider in these units.

These are :-

1.   THE **REPEATED MEASURES (or WITHIN SUBJECTS) DESIGN**

2.   THE **INDEPENDENT (or BETWEEN) SUBJECTS DESIGN**

3.   **MATCHED SUBJECTS DESIGN**

1. THE REPEATED MEASURES DESIGN

This design, is one within which each Subject experiences both conditions of the INDEPENDENT VARIABLE. We could say, that the study is carried out by working 'within' the one group of Subjects.

For example, using the above design in our Experiment investigating the effect of alcohol on driving skills, each driver experiences both conditions of the I.V. i.e. :-

The No Alcohol condition

and

The Alcohol condition.

This design offers advantages and disadvantages ....

(contd.)

- It is economic in its use of Subjects. As each Subject experiences both conditions of the Independent Variable, we require only half the number required for the Independent Subjects Design

- Each Subject acts as his own 'Control' i.e. If each Subject experiences both conditions of the I.V., then his basic abilities, intelligence, attitude, aptitude etc. are 'carried with him' and thus remain the same under each of the Experimental conditions.

- As the number of Subjects is halved, so is the incidence of individuals' differences such as, skill, ability to drive, ability to 'handle drink' etc.

Disadvantages :

- **Order or Practice effects -**

As each Subject has two trials, his performance may be enhanced in the second trial, as a result of practice gained in the first. To counteract this it is customary to alternate the trials i.e. one Subject carries out tasks in the order A then B, the next Subject experiences the order, B then A and so on. In this manner, the potentially positive practice effects are counterbalanced. Another consequence of having Subs. carry out one trial after the other is boredom or fatigue. Through this, the second trial or performance may suffer through fatigue or boredom, resulting from the first trial To avoid this, a delay between trials could be introduced

- **Treatment Carry Over Effects -**

Subjects' performance may be affected simply by their having experienced the first condition, e.g. they may feel more at ease, less anxious for the second trial as a result of taking part in the first. This is difficult to counteract and in some cases the 'carry over' may have a lasting effect as in the case of the learning of a skill by Subs. For example, if (non - cycling) Subjects had to learn to ride a bicycle in the first part of study, they would be rendered unsuitable for trial B, if it required non - cyclists. Having once learned a particular skill or sequence of events, the Subject is unlikely to forget this even after some considerable delay. To overcome this, one method is to purposely mislead Subs. as to the true nature or subject of the study. Having been thus mislead they will have no clue as to which particular skills are relevant to the next trial. However, in the case of the above 'cyclist' study this would be difficult to do. Psychologists have become quite adept at devising means of hiding the true intentions of their studies from Subjects. To a point this is acceptable but, at the end of the Experiment all Subjects should be fully 'debriefed' and the true purpose of the study explained to them.

2. THE INDEPENDENT SUBJECTS (or BETWEEN SUBJECTS) DESIGN

Turning now to the second design, we shall see that many of the disadvantages of the Repeated Measures design are in fact, the advantages of the Independent Subjects Design and vice versa.

This design operates 'between' two different groups of people. To return to our alcohol and driving Experiment, we could utilise two different groups of drivers and each group would then experience only one condition of the Independent Variable, either alcohol or no alcohol. Subjects would initially be allocated to one group or the other using some random selection process, e.g. tossing a coin.

- One group would drive (once) only in the no alcohol condition.

and

- One group would drive (once) only after consuming alcohol.

Advantages :

- Practice and Carry Over Effects -

  Such as fatigue or boredom are totally eliminated, as are any benefits through practice effects, e.g. learning in, or from the first trial.

- Order effects are eliminated.

Disadvantages :

- Not economical in the use of Subjects.

  Twice as many are required as for Repeated Measures, therefore time to complete the Experiment is extended, as are costs and staff involved. In addition, the practical aspects such as booking suitable facilities and equipment, assembling Subjects etc. are all doubled.

- Subjects no longer act as their 'own Control' :-

  It could just happen, if you were very unlucky, that Subjects in one group may be more intelligent, more skilled at driving, have faster reflexes, higher tolerance to alcohol etc. than in the other group. Comparisons of their group performances could thus be said to be unfair.

  However, in reality, the process involved in selecting groups of Subs. should, if conducted properly, ensure that the groups are 'equally representative of their parent population' and sufficiently large as to offset these individual differences.

3. MATCHED SUBJECTS (PAIRS) DESIGN

This design matches, as far as is practicable, the Subjects in the two Experimental groups. They are matched on factors which are deemed to be important or relevant to the study.

> For example we might ensure that Subjects are matched for age, occupation, I.Q., personality, attitudes, sex. In this way we may ensure that the two groups are as, initially identical as possible. Any differences in performance we may deduce to be the result of the experimental conditions.

SAQ

- Give two advantages of the Repeated Measures Design.

- Give two advantages of the Independent Subjects Design.

- Give two disadvantages for each of the above designs.

- Describe some typical ways in which we might try to 'match' Subjects if we intended using the Matched Subjects Design ?

UNIT 8 - EXPERIMENTAL DESIGN

```
******************************************************
******************************************************
******************** EXERCISE UNIT ********************
******************************************************
******************************************************
```

Please complete the following exercise unit and return your worksheet to your subject tutor

1   In a study to investigate the effect of noise upon Subjects' ability to concentrate. A psychologist arranges for one group of Subs. to attempt to solve a crossword while wearing headphones which relay loud music. Another group performs the same task without the loud music.

a) Which design is employed in this study

b) Identify the Independent and the Dependent Variables.

c) Could you suggest any controls which you think should have been applied.

d) Do you feel that the repeated measures design may be more, or less suitable for this study.

2.   Suppose you wish to investigate the proposition that the information Subjects are presented with first is most influential in the formation of their impressions. You use two passages of text, both describe an imaginary character called Tom. One begins with a description which presents Tom as friendly and outgoing, but then changes to present a much more reserved image. The other passage uses exactly the same text, but the order is reversed (i.e. Tom is presented first as reserved and then as outgoing). After reading the text, Subs. are asked to rate their impressions of Tom, as either Extravert or Introvert.

a) Which design would you use and why?

b) Are there any controls you would apply?

c) Do you feel that this study would tell us much about the manner in which people form impressions of others in real life situations?

PROGRESS BOX FOR UNIT 8

Review the unit and decide, were there any points you feel that you should revise or discuss with your tutor?

Do you understand all of the 'Keywords'?

Use the box below to record your progress :-

KEYWORDS FOR UNIT 8 :-

REPEATED MEASURES, INDEPENDENT SUBJECTS, MATCHED - SUBJECTS, PRACTICE EFFECT, CARRY OVER EFFECT

Revision Areas :-

....

....

....

....

....

....

....

....

UNIT 9 - ETHICAL CONSIDERATIONS

IN EXPERIMENTATION

When involving individuals in Experimental studies, some consideration must be given to protect them in terms of their health, privacy and individual dignity. To ensure this the American Psychological Society has drawn up a code of practice, which offers guidelines in this matter.

1.   The Experimenter should ensure that Subjects in the Experiment are not exposed to undue risks or hazards.

2.   He should ensure that all Subjects receive 'proper' treatment from assistants, **collaborators***, students and employees who are involved in the study.

3.   He should ensure that all Subjects are aware of what is expected of them during their participation in the Experiment. He should explain all aspects of the study which could (possibly) affect their willingness to participate. In addition he should take all reasonable steps to safeguard the welfare and dignity of the Subjects.

4.   Methodological requirements may necessitate the use of some concealment or deception. Before commencement the Experimenter should :-

     •   Investigate other methods, not using deception

     •   Determine whether the area of study involved justifies the use of such deception.

          After the Experiment, all Subjects should be "debriefed" and any deceptions explained (Read Stanley Milgram's (1974) Expt. on Obedience and evaluate the deception used).

5.   The Experimenter should recognise Subjects' right to decline to participate in, or withdraw from the Experiment. Remember, the Experimenter is in a privileged position whereby he may exert some authority or influence over Subs.

6.   The Experimenter should protect Subjects from Mental and Physical discomfort during the Experiment.

7.   After the collection of data the Experimenter should inform the Subjects of the nature of the study and its purpose and allay any misconceptions which may have arisen.

8.   Should any undesirable consequences arise from the conduct of the experiment, the Experimenter has an obligation to detect and where possible, remove these consequential effects.

9. All information obtained about a Subject during the course of the experiment must be held in confidence by the Experimenter unless some alternative agreement exists. Usually this would be explained to the Subject prior to commencement of the study.

In addition to the above items, one really ought to consider factors which are sometimes less obvious.

● We should ensure that the methods used in the study do not cause embarrassment or anxiety. For example we should check, before applying blindfolds whether the Subject is quite happy with this. If they aren't they should be allowed to drop out.

● If carrying out street interviews, ensure Subs. are safe from passing traffic etc.

● One 'infamous' study involved (young) Experimenters assessing the 'older generations' reactions to the use of bad language. Passers by were stopped and asked if they would mind taking part in a survey. If they agreed they were asked to record their reactions to a list of words. The words early in the list were quite innocuous, but as the reader progressed, more extreme language was used. Apparently, the reactions of some Subjects was to say the least, impressive. A clear case of a lack of consideration here.

UNIT 9 - ETHICS OF EXPERIMENTATION

```
******************************************************
******************************************************
********************* EXERCISE UNIT *********************
******************************************************
******************************************************
```

Please complete the following exercise unit and return your worksheet to your subject tutor

- Read an account of Stanley Milgram's famous study of Obedience carried out in 1963. Do feel that this study was 'ethical'? If not, then state how or why you feel it was not ethical.

GLOSSARY OF TERMS

COLLABORATOR   -   Usually a member of the Psychologist's research team who poses as a naive Subject in the Experiment. often called a 'stooge'.

PROGRESS BOX FOR UNIT 9.

Review the unit and decide, were there any points you feel that you should revise or discuss with your tutor?

Do you understand all of the 'Keywords' ?

Use the box below to record your progress :-

KEYWORDS FOR UNIT 9 :-

COLLABORATOR.

Revision Areas :-

....

....

....

....

....

....

....

....

....

UNIT 10 - AN INTRODUCTION TO STATISTICAL ANALYSIS

The results, or empirical data gathered from our studies have little or no value until such time as we apply some form of analysis to them. This analysis is carried out with the aid of statistical tests. These tests enable us to decide whether, or not, our research has produced results which we feel are important in the light of our hypothesis.

We may be able to observe a difference between the scores or results obtained from two groups in a study but, how can we be sure that this difference is sufficiently large, to be important and thus deemed to be a real outcome of our research situation?

We have already met the term Hypothesis and have established that this is in fact, a type of prediction which we set out to test.

To recap - If we find that our prediction has been true, then we say that the hypothesis has been supported. If not, we say the hypothesis has been rejected.

You may recall that there are two ways in which an hypothesis may be expressed :-

THE NULL HYPOTHESIS (abbreviated to Ho)

or

THE ALTERNATIVE HYPOTHESIS (abbreviated to H_1)

Let's look at another imaginary Experiment and its hypothesis :-

We wish to investigate the influence of group size, upon bystanders' intervention in some emergency situation. We could devise an Experiment and 'stage a scene' in a busy city street. We may involve two actors and have them act out a 'situation' where a large youth could push a young woman about. Inevitably a crowd will form around the incident and we might suppose that at some point, a member, or members of the crowd will step in to intervene and help the 'victim'.

Thus, we may hypothesise that :-

- As the number of bystanders increases, the delay in intervention will decrease - i.e the greater the crowd the greater the chance of assistance. This would be the Alternative hypothesis.

Or, on the other hand, we could state that :-

The number of bystanders in the group will have no effect upon
the speed of intervention. The Null hypothesis.

Just as matter of interest, research in this particular area suggests that group size does indeed have an effect upon potential intervention. However, that effect is quite the opposite to that suggested by 'common sense'. In most situations, the smaller the group, the greater the likelihood of some intervention'. So, if you're being beaten up, make sure you have only a small crowd watching.

However, to return to the above hypotheses, we have predicted a relationship between two variables, one is group size, the other, speed of intervention, each of which are observable and most importantly, 'measurable'. The data we collect would be - size of group (in numbers) and time for intervention (in seconds or minutes). Both types of data would be recorded in a record sheet, or table and then used for some later analysis.

A fairly crude way of analysing data is to calculate the 'mean' of any data we collect. In our 'bystander study' we might stage 100 'street scenes' and from these collect many different timings for a given group size. The timings would obviously vary, so we could calculate the mean time. The technical name for the 'mean' is called a measure of central tendency.

MEASURES OF CENTRAL TENDENCY

In statistics, you will often encounter the term 'the mean'. The word actually refers to what we commonly refer to, as an average - i.e all scores are added together and divided by the total number of scores. So in general usage, the word average is frequently misapplied. Average, is a term which embraces three differing types of 'average'.

These three are:

The Mean, The Median and The Mode and each of these is a Measure of Central tendency. The term, a 'Measure of Central Tendency', is simply another name for an 'Average' which is the single number which best represents the set of numbers from which it is drawn.

The three types of average are discussed below and each offers a particular advantage when used in the analysis of data.

THE MEAN :-

The mean is the average we are most used to. We arrive at the mean by adding together the values of a set of numbers and then divide by the number (of numbers) in the set.

(contd.)

However, the mean is affected by the magnitude (size) of individual scores and thus, one very high or very low score in a series will greatly alter or shift the value of the mean.

For example, let's look at the numbers :

6, 7, 6, 3, 6, 8, 6, 8 they would produce a MEAN of ....

$6 + 7 + 6 + 3 + 6 + 8 + 6 + 8 \div 8 = 6.25$

However if we now placed the number 60 in the series, the mean would become

$6 + 7 + 6 + 3 + 6 + 8 + 6 + 8 + 60 \div 9 = 12.22$

The Mean is said to be influenced by EXTREME scores i.e. if we have some very large or very small scores in the set, they will 'pull' the value of the mean up or down toward them.

The symbol for the MEAN is $\overline{X}$ and is called 'bar X' and the formula for its calculation is shown by the symbols :-

$$\frac{\sum x}{N}$$

Where $\sum$ (called Sigma) means 'the sum of' all the individual (x) scores. Divided by N the total number of scores.

THE MEDIAN-

To find the Median we must first sort our set of numbers in order of rank, in ascending order - i.e. Smallest to Largest.

For example if we had 10, 6, 25, 112, 9

They would be sorted in to rank order ... 6, 9, 10, 25, 112

10 is the MIDDLE number and so the MEDIAN = 10

If the total number of scores in the set is even, an average (or Mean) of the two central scores is taken

e.g. 10, 6, 25, 112, 9, 27 = 6, 9, 10, 25, 27, 112

Central scores are 10 and 25, so the MEDIAN = (10 + 25) ÷ 2 = 17.5

Note! - The Median is much less affected by EXTREME scores. If we added the number 250 on to the end of our series - i.e.

10, 6, 25, 112, 9, 27, 250 = 6, 9, 10, 25, 27, 112, 250

The Median is now 25.

THE MODE

The MODE is quite simply, the number which occurs most frequently in a series

If we had the set ....   6, 7, 6, 3, 6, 8, 6,   The MODE of this series is 6 - i.e. we have more occurrences of 6 than any other number.

NOTE! It is possible to have more than one value for a mode

e.g. 6, 7, 6, 3, 3, 6, 8, 6, 3, 2, 3

In this set we have two modes i.e. 6 and 3, thus it is 'Bi Modal'. In practice, any set with more than three modes is simply called **'Multimodal'**

In summary, the Mean is probably the most important average of the three discussed. It does give us important information about the data we are dealing with and many statistical tests are based around the information derived from it. It deals with the actual 'values' of the numbers we are dealing with. The median is concerned only with their 'ranked' position and is thus less powerful. The mode deals only with 'frequency of occurrence' and is the least useful of the three.

If we look at naturally occurring events in the world around us, for example peoples' shoe sizes, we find that they vary enormously. We have a few with very small feet, some with very large feet and in the middle, the bulk of the population (the mean) who are all of 'average size'.

If we drew a graph of peoples' shoe sizes we would produce a graph with a curve shaped rather like an bell. This bell shape is called the 'Normal Distribution Curve', it shows quite graphically what a 'mean' is and will be discussed in a later section.

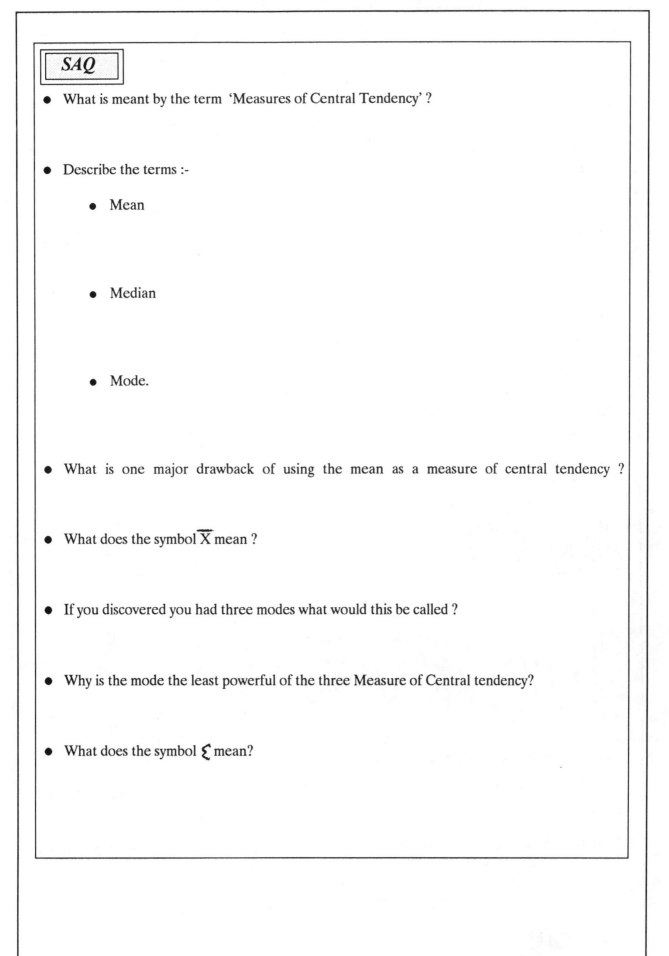

SAQ

- What is meant by the term 'Measures of Central Tendency' ?

- Describe the terms :-

  - Mean

  - Median

  - Mode.

- What is one major drawback of using the mean as a measure of central tendency ?

- What does the symbol $\overline{X}$ mean ?

- If you discovered you had three modes what would this be called ?

- Why is the mode the least powerful of the three Measure of Central tendency?

- What does the symbol Σ mean?

UNIT 10 - INTRODUCTION TO STATISTICAL ANALYSIS

```
**********************************************************
**********************************************************
********************* EXERCISE UNIT *********************
**********************************************************
**********************************************************
```

Please complete the following exercise unit and return your worksheet to your subject tutor

1. A psychologist collected the following two sets of test results in a study. The numbers are in fact scores at a maths test and marked out of a possible maximum score of 100.

Group 1		Group 2	
Subject	Score	Subject	Score
1	67	1	86
2	76	2	94
3	55	3	59
4	88	4	46
5	77	5	65
6	66	6	66
7	56	7	87
8	58	8	88
9	80	9	76
10	80	10	54
11	71	11	59
12	65	12	65
13	83	13	65
14	54	14	67
15	80	15	43

Calculate the mean, median and mode for each group.

What do these measures of central tendency tell us about the relative performance of the two groups

If the hypothesis of the study had stated that Group 1 would perform better than Group 2, would it have been supported ?

RECOMMENDED READING

EXPERIMENT, DESIGN AND STATISTICS IN PSYCHOLOGY - C. Robson

PROGRESS BOX FOR UNIT 10

Review the unit and decide, were there any points you feel that you should revise or discuss with your tutor?
Do you understand all of the 'Keywords' ?

Use the box below to record your progress :-

KEYWORDS FOR UNIT 10 :-

MEAN, MEDIAN, MODE, MEASURES OF CENTRAL TENDENCY
NORMAL DISTRIBUTION CURVE, MULTIMODAL

Revision Areas :-

....

....

....

....

....

....

....

....

....

....

UNIT 11 - THE CORRELATION

The word Correlation, when used in the statistical sense, may be loosely interpreted as an 'association' or relationship between two events.

If two sets of variables show a CORRELATION, then it may be said that there is some association between them. This association between events is apparent as some form of consistent **COVARIATION** between them - i.e as one event varies, then so does the other.

We could, for example say that there is a CORRELATION between the size of peoples' foot size and their height - as they get taller, so their feet get larger (if this didn't happen, they would blow over in high winds).

NOTE! - It is important to remember that although the two events may be connected or associated in some way, one need not necessarily CAUSE the other

Lets look at an example to illustrate the pitfalls of assuming that CORRELATION and **CAUSALITY** are one and the same thing .....

It may be observed that on very hot days Guardsmen in London are prone to falling over whilst on the parade ground.

We may also note that on these same hot days, the tar covering the parade ground is soft. This is an example of a CORRELATION and so, we can quite safely say that :-

ON DAYS WHEN TAR IS SOFT GUARDSMEN FALL OVER

i.e. the two events are associated or CORRELATED - thus far ,we are quite correct.

Now, because these two events appear to occur together, could we go one stage further and suggest that the soft tar affects the Guardsmens' balance and thus causes them to fall over ?

If we did then we would be implying causality where in fact, none exists. In this case, we would have missed one vitally important causal factor. Namely the heat of the sun and its consequent effect upon the Guards' state of health.

Another example ....

We may, on occasion see a gathering of people on a station platform and within a short period, a train appears in the distance, it stops, all the people board it and they are whisked away.

Here we have a CORRELATION (or association) between two events.

To an observer not well versed in the ways of British Rail, it could appear that in order to travel by rail, all that is required is to assemble a set number of people on a station platform and by some almost magical process a train will soon appear and carry them off.

These examples, although rather extreme and simplistic do illustrate an important point. Before jumping to the conclusion that one event causes another (i.e. that CAUSALITY exists), we must carefully evaluate all other possible associated factors and examine them for their potential effects.

To offer a more realistic example ....

Research has suggested that there is a link between an increased incidence of lung cancer and heart disease in people who smoke cigarettes. In the face of this correlational evidence, it would appear reasonable to assume a 'causal link' and say "Cigarettes cause lung cancer and heart disease"

In reality, the case is not so clear cut, or obvious - Why ?

- Can we be sure that the type of people who are predisposed to smoking may not share some common genetic factor which predisposes them to develop lung cancer or heart disease ?

- Can we be sure that all those who smoke do not share other similar factors which increases their likelihood of developing lung cancer and heart disease. For example some common personality traits ?

- The fact that some people smoke, may in itself point to the fact that they are less able to cope with stress. Thus, they may be more affected by it than others who do not resort to smoking as a form of coping with stress. Alternatively, it may indicate that they as individuals have a more stressful lifestyle, which in itself may lead to later serious health problems.

- It may even be, that all those who smoke share two common factor. One, which makes them want to smoke 'and' some 'cancer factor' which makes them more disposed to cancer.

- Modern Urban life is said to be faster and more stressful than that enjoyed by previous generations. Many of our Grandparents smoked and lived to a ripe old age. Could it be the case that lung cancer is caused by smoking AND living in our more stressful times. Perhaps there are other factors which we are exposed to today. For example, exhaust fumes, food additives, general pollution, all of which, in conjunction with smoking may cause a greater incidence of these diseases which are often referred to as the diseases of affluence. If we could turn the clock back 100 years could we smoke and suffer no risks to our health ?

There are doubtless many other aspects of this argument which could be examined but, to summarise -

We must exercise some caution when proposing any 'CAUSAL' link between two variables which simply show a Correlation.

We now turn to the types of CORRELATION we may encounter.

There are three :-

- POSITIVE CORRELATION

- ZERO CORRELATION

- NEGATIVE CORRELATION

Within this learning package, we will look at two ways of assessing the degree of Correlation between two variables ..

1. Diagrammatically - using a diagram or graph called a **SCATTERGRAM**

and later

2. Using a calculation called SPEARMAN'S RHO or another called PEARSON'S 'r'

The diagrammatic system of showing a correlation uses a type of graph called a SCATTERGRAM.

Let's look at an example of a POSITIVE CORRELATION

If we imagine a situation in which we wish compare students' exam scores with the number of lectures they attend. We are in fact, looking for some relationship or association between the exam scores obtained by the students and the number of lectures they attended. We could be naive and assume that the more lectures they attend, the better will be their scores.

(Cont'd)

81

If this is the case, then given the data below, we would find a Positive Correlation between the two - as one increases, so does the other :-

Student No.	1	2	3	4	5	6	7	8	9	10
Score (%)	15	30	40	45	10	20	80	85	70	10
No. of Lecs.	10	10	20	15	5	15	28	30	25	12

The above scores could be drawn up and plotted in a graph called a SCATTERGRAM (see below).

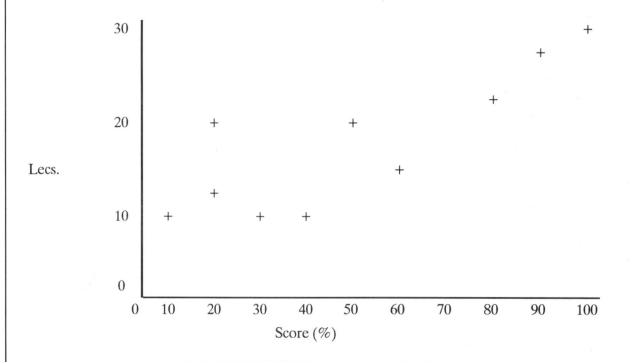

A POSITIVE CORRELATION

Note! The Scattergram for a positive correlation falls into a 'cigar shape' or line running from bottom left, to top right. To remember it, think of a 'tick'. At school, we used to get ticks for positive results.

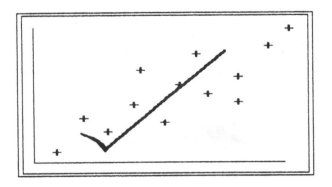

However, if we look at the same situation but with a different set of scores and lecture attendances :-

Student No.	1	2	3	4	5	6	7	8	9	10
Score (%)	80	30	40	45	35	20	45	25	40	70
No. of Lecs.	10	10	20	15	5	15	28	30	25	12

Here, we find that the attendance of lectures and exam scores shows no consistent relationship, i.e some people who attended a large number of lectures got low scores and some who attended very few got higher scores. We now have a ZERO CORRELATION.

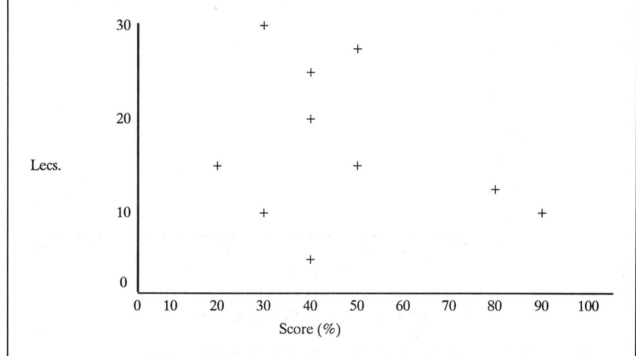

A ZERO CORRELATION

Note! The Scattergram shows no distinct pattern, in fact a zero correlation often falls into a '0' shape.

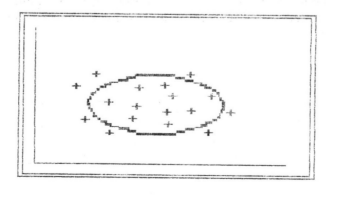

Finally we could have a NEGATIVE CORRELATION, i.e. as one variable increases the other decreases :-

Student No.	1	2	3	4	5	6	7	8	9	10
Score (%)	85	80	40	55	90	50	15	10	15	80
No. of Lecs.	10	10	20	15	5	15	28	30	25	12

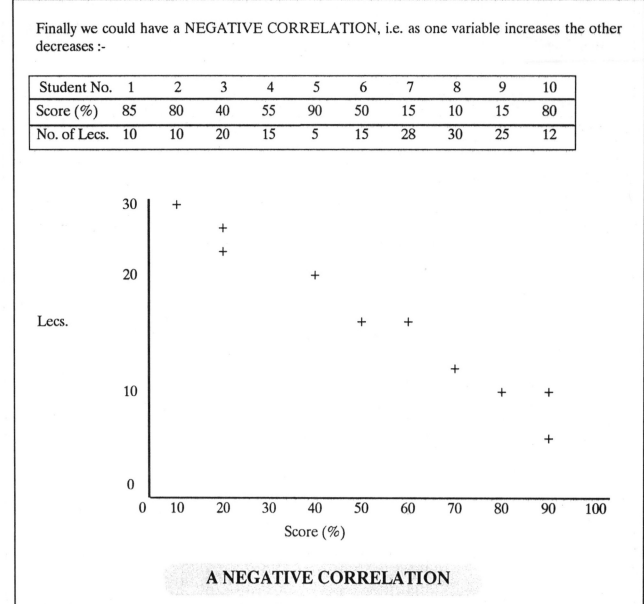

A NEGATIVE CORRELATION

Note! - We now find a pattern which is the reverse of the positive correlation.

Each of the above scattergrams produce a very distinctive pattern and from these patterns, we are able to assess by eye, the degree of correlation, or association between two sets of data.

There are however, occasions when we really need to know rather more than the graphical information provided above. On these occasions we utilise one of the statistical tests which allow some 'numerical' evaluation of the degree of correlation. From the results of these tests, we may decide whether the correlation between our observed data sets is 'significant' and thus of any importance to our study.

SAQ

- If you were told that, as the pressure of a gas rises, then so does its temperature. What sort of correlation is this?

- What is meant by the term 'covariance or covariation'?

- If we found a positive correlation between eating seafood and weight gain what does this suggest?

- If we found a zero correlation between playing 'piped music' in a supermarket and sales of food. What does this suggest?

- Given that there is a strong positive correlation between two events, may we assume that one 'caused' the other?

UNIT 11 - THE CORRELATION

```
****************************************************
****************************************************
******************** EXERCISE UNIT ********************
****************************************************
****************************************************
```

Please complete the following exercise unit and return your worksheet to your subject tutor

1. The results shown below are those collected for the previous Exercise unit. Plot a scattergram of group 1's scores against group 2's. What type of correlation does this show ?

Group 1.		Group 2.	
Subject	Score	Subject	Score
1	67	1	86
2	76	2	94
3	55	3	59
4	88	4	46
5	77	5	65
6	66	6	66
7	56	7	87
8	58	8	88
9	80	9	76
10	80	10	54
11	71	11	59
12	65	12	65
13	83	13	65
14	54	14	67
15	80	15	43

(Contd.)

2. If we were to examine the scores of children in maths and reading tests we may find that there is a relationship between the two i.e. children who are good readers may also prove to be good at maths.

   To assess the type of relationships and degree of correlation, use the results in table 1 and draw a Scattergram

Example 1

Results - Table 1

Child	1	2	3	4	5	6	7	8	9	10	11	12
Maths Score	9	10	12	6	11	9	12	16	13	10	13	14
Reading	2	3	1	1	4	1	5	8	5	3	6	7

Example 2

A different group of children produced the results shown below in table 2. Carry out the same procedure as in the exercise above.

Results - Table 2

Child	1	2	3	4	5	6	7	8	9	10	11	12
Maths Score	9	10	8	6	11	9	12	12	13	11	13	14
Reading	9	7	8	10	7	6	3	4	6	6	3	1

Note ! Reading scores were marked out of a possible 10 and maths out of a possible 20

PROGRESS BOX FOR UNIT 11

Review the unit and decide, were there any points you feel that you should revise or discuss with your tutor?

Do you understand all of the 'Keywords' ?

Use the box below to record your progress :-

KEYWORDS FOR UNIT 11 :-

POSITIVE CORRELATION, NEGATIVE CORRELATION, ZERO - CORRELATION, SCATTERGRAM, COVARIATION.

Revision Areas :-

....

....

....

....

....

....

....

....

....

UNIT 12 - BAR CHARTS, HISTOGRAMS and FREQUENCY DIAGRAMS

Graphs are used frequently to present the results of research studies and they present data in an easily assimilated form. The two types of graph we are interested in, are the Bar chart and the Histogram. In both, we generally plot the Independent Variable (I.V.) along the bottom 'X' axis and the Dependent Variable (D.V.) up the vertical 'Y' axis.

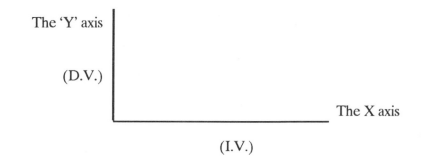

BAR CHARTS

In a bar chart we tend to be interested only in the 'numerical' values on the Y axis, as in the example below. Here the X axis represents the names of the Subjects enrolled at a College, these are called NOMINAL or DISCRETE values. The Y axis on the other hand, represents numerical values in this case the number of students enrolled on the courses.

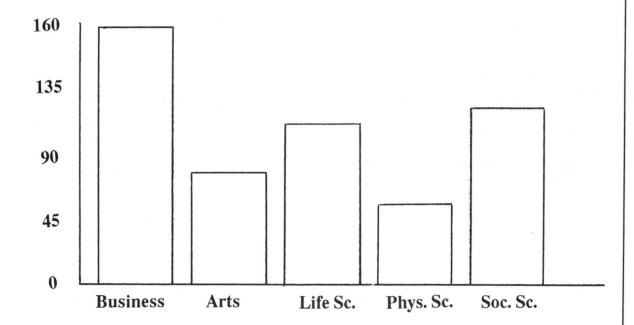

The bars in a 'bar' chart are drawn separately to avoid any suggestion that there is any (direct numeric) relationship between items placed along the 'X' axis.

HISTOGRAMS

The Histogram differs from the bar chart, in that we are interested in 'two' sets of numerical values. Both sets of data are of the Continuous type, this means that the data is Continuous in value and thus can be sub divided. This is quite unlike the data used on the X axis of the Bar Chart shown previously, where the data is usually 'named', as in Course names, Question numbers, number of children in families etc. Remember, this data type is called 'Nominal' or 'Discrete Data. Clearly with that type, there can be no between values, i.e we could have no 'half numbers' for number of children in families.

If we created a histogram to show the frequency of occurrence of heights of workers in a factory. We could divide up the X axis into sections, or intervals to catch all of the individuals who fall within the range of heights shown. I.E. all those who are between 4'7" and 4'9" are shown in the first bar, all those between 4'9" and 4'11" in the next and so on. In this way we can, plot all of those who fall within a certain range of heights (or scores) in one bar.

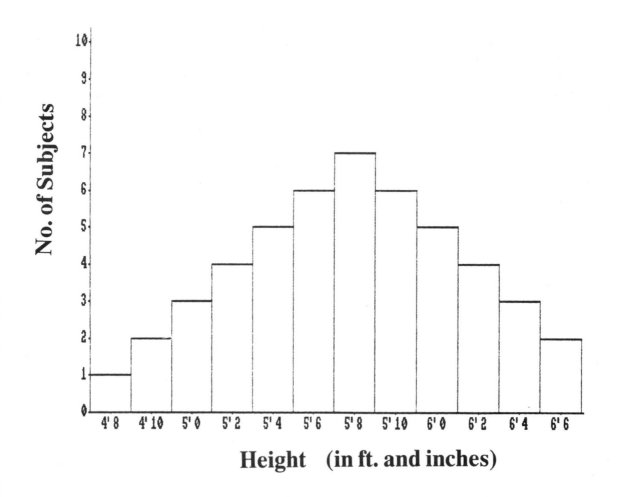

Height   (in ft. and inches)

Each bar is thus a 'step' or 'interval' and its width represents a real interval in terms of (in this case) the heights, or scores being recorded.

We now turn to a specific type of histogram, the so called **Frequency Diagram**. This is a type of graph which is of great interest to statisticians, the Frequency Diagram records the frequency, or number of occasions certain scores occur.

For example, given the table of data below, from a study where 25 Subjects could score from 1 to 6 in a test :-

Subject	1	2	3	4	5	6	7	8	9	10	11	12	13	14	15	16	17	18	19	20	21	22	23	24	25
Scores	5	6	3	4	2	2	1	3	4	2	1	5	4	3	3	1	2	6	2	5	4	6	3	5	2

Before drawing a frequency diagram, we could record the 'frequency' of data in a table as shown below. i.e. we would record how many times a Subject scored each individual score ... 1, 2, 3, 4 etc. :-

Score	1	2	3	4	5	6
Frequency	3	6	5	4	4	2

The new table shows that the score '1' occurred 3 times, '2' occurred 6 times, '3' occurred 5 times and so on. The frequency should of course, add up to 25, that being the total number of Subjects involved in the study. If we drew a frequency diagram of the above results, we would produce the graph below.

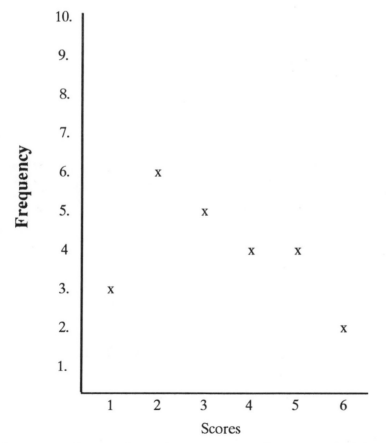

The frequency diagram is an important tool for the statistician and the manner in which information derived from it is discussed in more detail later.

SAQ

- In what way does a histogram differ from a bar chart?

- What does a 'frequency diagram' tell us?

- What type of data would you expect to be shown on the 'X' axis of a histogram?

PROGRESS BOX FOR UNIT 12.

Review the unit and decide, were there any points you feel that you should revise or discuss with your tutor?

Do you understand all of the 'Keywords' ?

Use the box below to record your progress :-

KEYWORDS FOR UNIT 12 :-

HISTOGRAM, BAR CHART, FREQUENCY DIAGRAM

Revision Areas :-

....

....

....

....

....

....

....

....

....

....

UNIT 13 - THE NORMAL DISTRIBUTION

Any events which occur naturally, when plotted in a frequency distribution, tend to produce a bell shaped curve. This bell shape is known as the Normal Distribution Curve.

The Normal Distribution Curve

Other names for this curve are :-

The **Gaussian Curve** (after Gauss the mathematician who first described it's properties)

The Normal Probability Curve

Most naturally occurring events fall into this type of distribution. For example, Peoples' heights, Weights, Intelligence (as measured by I.Q* tests) and as mentioned earlier, shoe sizes.

Let's take the example of I.Q testing. An I.Q. of 100 is the average and we find that in the population as a whole, there are those who, when tested will score above and those who will score below this average. If we were to plot a frequency diagram of I.Q test scores (as below), we would in fact produce a Normal Distribution Curve. At the far left we would have the scores of all of those who fall well below the 'average' intelligence. At the right, are those of very high intelligence and in the centre, the 'rest of us'.

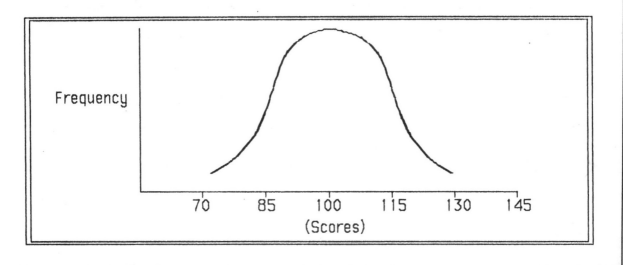

The Normal Distribution curve does have certain stable properties, which have proved to be extremely useful to statisticians.

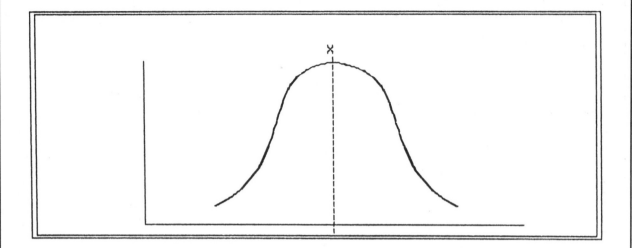

We know for instance, that the Mean, Median and Mode all fall at the centre point or peak of the curve (point X).

However, in reality we rarely get a perfect 'Normal Distribution' from our data. because our samples are very seldom totally representative of everyone, or everything in the parent population from which the sample was drawn. In other words we may have more people with large feet in our sample or vice versa, and so our curve will never be a perfect bell shape.

In most cases we will get some form of 'Skewed Curve', the 'Skew' may be positive or negative, both are shown below

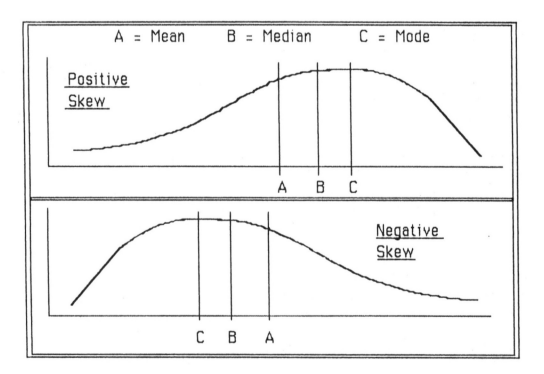

The effect of this 'Skew' is to pull the Mean away from the central point and toward the more extreme, end values.

STANDARD DEVIATION.

The **Standard Deviation** (abbreviated to SD) is a measure of DISPERSION. That is to say it gives us an indication as to how far the individual scores are spread or scattered around the Mean Score.

As you know, the Mean is the score or value, which is most representative of the whole set of data. It does tell us the 'central, or representative score, but it does not tell us how, or where the other values lie in relation to it. In simple terms, the Standard Deviation tells us :-

'How much (on average) the individual scores in the set differ from the Mean'.

Let's look at an example - Given the scores :-

$$6, 7, 8, 9, 10$$

The Mean is :- $\qquad 6 + 7 + 8 + 9 + 10 \div 5 = 8$

Now, the difference of each score, from the Mean (score - 8) is :-

$$(6 - 8), (7 - 8), (8 - 8), (9 - 8), (10 - 8)$$

$$= \qquad -2 \quad -1 \quad 0 \quad +1 \quad +2$$

We can now find the 'Average Difference', but, if we do this in the normal way i.e. by adding the scores and dividing by 5, we will have 0 divided by 5 and arrive at an answer of 0. Or, we could simply ignore the signs :-

$$2 + 1 + 0 + 1 + 2 \quad 5 = 1.2$$

Doing this would then tell us that the scores vary, on average from the mean (8) by + or - 1.2 .... This is called the **Mean Deviation.**

Sadly, this would not be considered 'Good Mathematical Practice'

A more acceptable system would be to calculate the individual differences from the mean, as above. Then square each of these individual results.

This would give us $(6 - 8)^2 + (7 - 8)^2 + (8 - 8)^2 + (9 - 8)^2 + (10 - 8)^2$

$$= 4 + 1 + 0 + 1 + 4 = 10 \quad \text{divided by } 5 = 2$$

This result is called the 'Mean Squared Deviation' and because the answer is squared, we must find the square root of the figure (2). The standard deviation is thus 1.414. This tells us that the scores vary ,on average 1.414 units from the mean score.

The Theoretical formula is $\qquad SD = \dfrac{\Sigma (X - X)^2}{N - 1}$

(contd.)

However, the formula we will use for the Standard Deviation is is easier to use on a calculator

$$SD = \sum \frac{X^2 - (\sum X)^2/N}{(N-1)}$$

The symbols are as below :

N	=	Total number of scores involved in the calculation.
$\sum X^2$	=	Square each (individual) score then add the results together.
$(\sum X)^2$	=	Add all the individual scores together, then square result.
/N	=	Divide by total 'number' of scores collected.
(N - 1)	=	Total number of scores minus 1.

We already know, that when results fall into the bell shaped pattern called the 'Normal Distribution', we can derive a great deal of information from this curve. If we move out along the X axis, away from the mean by specific distances, we know that there will be a specific percentage of the population (whose scores are represented by the curve) falling under that section of the curve.

The distances, measured as 'z' scores from the mean are actually expressed as 'parts' of the Standard Deviation i.e. - a 'z' score of 1.5 is a position moved 1.5 Standard Deviations, out from the mean.

In fact, if we measure out from each side of the mean by one Standard Deviation (or a 'z' score of 1) 68.26% of the population will be enclosed by that section of the curve. This is divided into two parts, note that 34.13% falls either side of the mean which is at position 0 - See below

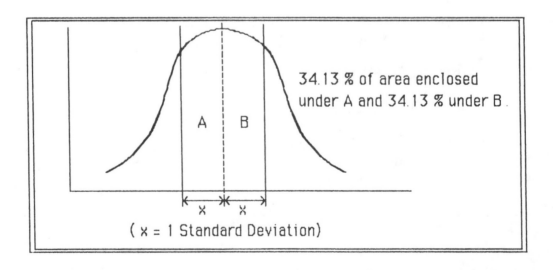

34.13 % of area enclosed under A and 34.13 % under B.

A | B

(x = 1 Standard Deviation)

Staying with the Standard Distribution :-

If we move out either side of the mean by a 'z' score of 1.96, remember this means 1.96 x the standard deviation, we find that 95% of the sample is enclosed within that section of the curve. The remaining 5% (2.5% at each end) fall under the outside tails of the curve.

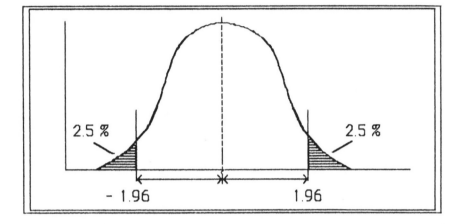

This notion of the areas enclosed by the Normal Distribution is of critical importance to our assessment of the importance or 'significance' of our statistical findings and is discussed in the next Unit.

SAQ

- What shape is the 'Gaussian Curve' and what is it ?

- What does a frequency diagram tell us ?

- What is meant by the terms, positive and negative skew ?

- What does The Standard Deviation show ?

- What is a 'z' score ?

- What percentage of the population falls under the two extreme tails of the Normal Distribution   (z scores of 1.96)

- How many S.D.'s would a 'z' score of 1.74 be (away) from the mean?

GLOSSARY

I.Q. (Intelligence Quotient)   -   An age related measure of intelligence, in which the Subjects' mental age is divided by his chronological age (in years). The mental age is assessed by means of a test and the result of this comparison yields a number. This number is the Sub's. I.Q. 100 being the standard or average I.Q. i.e. when mental and chronological age are the same.

SUGGESTED READING

Experiment, Design and Statistics in Psychology
- Colin Robson.

PROGRESS BOX FOR UNIT 13.

Review the unit and decide, were there any points you feel that you should revise or discuss with your tutor?

Do you understand all of the 'Keywords' ?

Use the box below to record your progress :-

KEYWORDS FOR UNIT 13 :-

GAUSSIAN CURVE, SKEW, STANDARD DEVIATION, DISPERSION, MEAN DEVIATION, MEAN SQUARED DEVIATION, 'Z' SCORES.

Revision Notes:-

....

....

....

....

....

....

....

....

....

UNIT 14 - THE LEVEL OF STATISTICAL SIGNIFICANCE.

In an earlier unit, we mentioned the term 'Significance' in relation to the decision process undertaken when analysing results. Thus, having acquired some results for any groups in our study, we must decide whether any differences in their performance, as reflected in their mean scores, is sufficiently great or important to be noteworthy.

Let us review an example we looked at in an earlier unit. We had a situation where we set out to test the effectiveness of a new system of teaching primary school children to read. We had one group taught under the traditional system, another with the new system. At the end of a predetermined period we tested all of the children and recorded each group's results. We would almost certainly find 'some difference' in the mean scores of the the two groups. What we need to be sure of is, just how 'big' must this difference be for us to be certain that the new teaching system is really worthwhile? In statistical terms, we say that if a difference is large enough to be considered important, then it is a Significant result.

Well, common sense tells us that if we are to judge the new system successful, any differences we find must be greater than those we would expect to find simply by chance. Clearly, we would expect to see some differences, even if we tested two groups of children using the 'same reading system'. We must therefore be sure, that any differences we do find, are 'totally' due to our having one group taught under one system and the other under the new system and not just, the 'expected' differences we could find by chance.

Returning to our two groups of school children, group A and group B. If we marked their tests out of 100 then we could, arrive at the following mean scores :-

CLASS A = 50   CLASS B = 61

Now, here we have some difference (11), but is it large enough to be considered 'important'? What about these scores -

CLASS A = 50   CLASS B = 62 is that better ? (diff. = 12)

or, consider the scores

CLASS A = 50   CLASS B = 100 (diff. = 50)

In this last case, we would probably feel fairly confident with this size of difference and could reasonably assume that class B's teaching method was producing better results.

Sadly, in real life research, we rarely achieve such obviously large differences in scores in our Experimental work and so we must look for some universally acceptable level of difference, which we will consider large enough, or important.

In their attempts to find a measure of difference, which can be said to be sufficiently large to indicate a real 'difference between groups', statisticians have resorted to the properties of the Normal Distribution Curve.

If you recall, in our earlier discussion of this curve, we said that by selecting points at given distances, measured as 'z' scores (out) from the mean, we know that certain percentages of the sample or population will fall into the area enclosed below the curve.

Remember, if we measure out from each side of the mean by a distance of one Standard Deviation, or a 'z' score of 1, then 68.26% of the population will be enclosed by that section of the curve, 34.13% falling either side of the mean. See below.

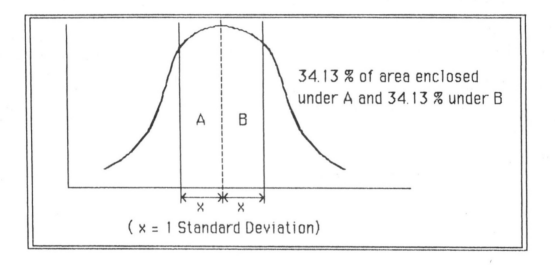

34.13 % of area enclosed under A and 34.13 % under B

(x = 1 Standard Deviation)

If however, we move out further, to a 'z' score 1.96 from the mean (remember, this means 1.96 x the S.D.) we will enclose 95% of the population under the curve. Leaving 2.5% of the population under the two tails of the curve. See below.

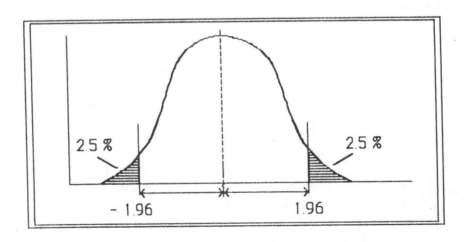

2.5 %   2.5 %

- 1.96   1.96

Over time, Statisticians and Scientists in general have agreed on a convention or a level of difference. They have agreed that if two groups performances differ by this (agreed) amount, then it indicates that the difference between them is said to be SIGNIFICANT.

This agreed difference is called the 5% level of significance and to understand quite what it means, we must once more return to the Normal Distribution Curve.

Let us imagine that two groups (A & B) perform a task and each are scored for their performance. If both performed in exactly the same way, we would find that the means for each group were identical, there would be no difference.

If we drew a distribution curve for each, on the same axis, the two curves would sit exactly one on top of the other. Now let us imagine that group B performs better than group A. We would find that if we now drew both of their curves on the same axes, group B's would be shifted some distance to the right (assuming higher scores are to the right). As the difference increases, so the curves would separate more and more.

In the example below, we have two groups' distributions which would be said to be significantly different:-

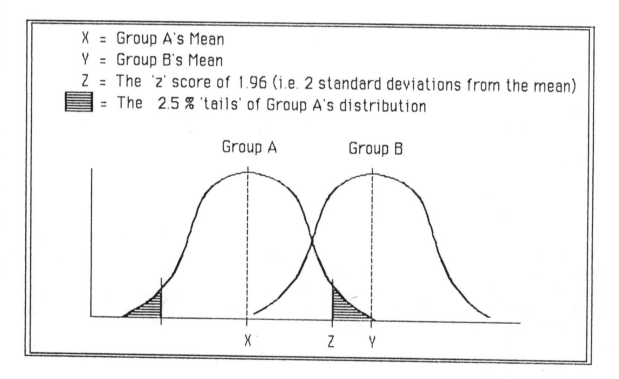

We say that we have a significant difference if we obtain a difference between two groups' mean scores, such that it shifts one group's curve or distribution over to one side by a 'z' score of as much as 1.96. One curve has shifted so far to the right, group B in this case, that its mean falls into that part of Group A's curve which encloses only 2.5% of its (group A's) population.

In simple terms we are saying that if the mean of one group shifted this far, then we we will accept this level of difference as being unlikely to have been caused by chance factors alone. We will then surmise that the 'shift' was caused by our Experimental manipulations. What this means in terms of probability is, that the difference we have at the 5% level, is so great as to happen by chance only 1 time in 20. Or, on 5% of all occasions.

Let's convert this so called 5% significance into everyday events. We could say that if our chance of crossing the road and being hit by a bus was 50% this would mean that for every two times we crossed a road we could expect to run down on one of them. Odds of 1 in 2, not very good.

Bus - What Bus ?

If however, the level of chance was changed to 5%, this means that for every 20 times we cross, on 19 we will be O.K. but on one occasion we will risk being squashed. Much better odds (1 in 20) and the same ones as Social Scientists work at.

Thus, in the Social Sciences it is generally accepted that if the probability of something happening by chance is less than 5% (less than 5 times in a 100 or 1 in 20) we will regard this as acceptable and agree that the particular event occurred as a result of our Experimental situation.

HOW DO WE FIND OUT WHETHER A 'DIFFERENCE' IS SIGNIFICANT?

It is obviously time consuming and impractical, to draw graphs for every set of results we obtain, so in practice, we resort to the use of statistical tests. The raw data or raw scores, obtained during the study, are fed into the formula of a statistical test and result is calculated. This result is then compared to one shown in a table and from this comparison, a decision is made as to the significance of the Experimenter's calculated or observed result.

In the case of assessing the extent of a difference in mean scores, if the calculated value exceeds the one shown in the tables, we conclude that our result is indeed significant and the differences in performance between the two groups was indeed due to our 'experimental manipulations' and not simply a chance outcome.

Degrees of Freedom :

When referring to statistical tables we must calculate and utilise a figure referred to as the **DEGREE OF FREEDOM** (usually abbreviated to d.f.) in our study. The term frequently creates some confusion in those new to statistics, so it is worth devoting some time to an explanation.

Let us suppose that you are told that a set of 8 numbers, when totalled gave the result 45. If you were then told seven of the numbers and asked to find out the missing one :-

e.g. $12 + 4 + 10 + 5 + 3 + 5 + 2 + ?$

You would soon realise that the last one was :   4

In this example we would say that the degrees of freedom required to calculate the missing number was 7, i.e. we need to know at least seven of the numbers in order to calculate the value of the last one.

If, on the other hand, you were only told six of the numbers :

e.g. $12 + 4 + 10 + 5 + 3 + 5 + ? + ?$

You would be unable to know with certainty what the missing two were, (2 & 4). You would of course know that together they added up to 6, but that would be little help in finding their individual values.

In short, d.f. means the minimum number of items we need to know, in order to calculate any missing one.

Another example might be in the accommodation of ten people in a hotel with only ten vacant rooms. The first 9 have freedom to choose any room they wish, however the tenth person has, once all the others have chosen, only one choice of room - i.e the only one left. The degrees of freedom here are nine.

Degrees of Freedom in the world of experimental data is applied to the number of Subjects (N) used in the study or the number of groups of Subjects.

In general it is easy to calculate and is simply :-

Number of 'single' Subjects minus 1, usually expressed as N -1

or

Number of 'groups' of Subjects minus 1

For example,if we had two groups in a study, 5 Subs. in one group and 7 in the other, the df would be :- $(5 -1) + (7 -1) = 10$

		Significance levels		
d.f.	0.10	0.05	0.02	0.01
1	6.314	12.706	31.821	63.657
2	2.920	4.303	6.965	9.925
3	2.353	3.182	4.541	5.841
4	2.132	2.776	3.747	4.604
5	2.015	2.571	3.365	4.032

Above is an excerpt from a statistical table, it is used to evaluate the results of a statistical test (we will meet later) called the 't' test. The test assesses the difference in mean scores of two groups. Once the value of 't' is calculated, it is then compared to the tabled value. It is compared to the row which corresponds with our particular d.f. Let's say we have a d.f. of four, we then look across at (row) d.f. = 4, then, in the column relating to our significance level of 5% (.05) we see the tabled value is 2.776.

Thus for our calculated 't' test result to be significant it would have to greater than 2.776.

ONE AND TWO TAILED TESTS

When we formulate an hypothesis it is referred to as either **one or two** tailed. This means, that in the case of the a two tailed hypothesis, we are predicting only that there will be a 'difference' between the two groups' performance. We accept that a significant shift by one group, in either direction (above below the other's mean) would be considered to be 'significant'.

In some cases however, we may, before the study, make a prediction of the direction of the expected results. We may for example, predict that GROUP A will get higher scores than GROUP B., thus we are predicting a direction of difference.

The difference in using a one, as opposed to a two tailed hypothesis, is that when we come to consult our tables to assess significance. There are usually two rows at the head of the table, one for one tailed and the other for two tailed hypotheses.

In the past we have dealt with 5% as being split between the two tails (2.5% per side), in a one tailed test we are only interested in 5% at one end. So, to assess whether or not our result is significant we refer to the appropriate column.

We may now find that a result which was previously not considered significant at the 5% level, becomes significant at the 10% level shown in the tables.

SAQ

- When we refer to a result being 'significant', what do we really mean by this ?

- What is the agreed level of significance, as accepted by statisticians and social scientists ?

- What is the 5% level of significance when expressed in terms of odds (e.g. 1 in 5000 etc.) ?

- What does Degrees of Freedom mean ?

- How does a one tailed test differ from a two tailed test ?

- Which would require the greatest difference in means. A result significant at the 1% level or one significant at the 5% level ?

- What is a type one error ?

- Which type of error would most likely result from working to the 1% level ?

PROGRESS BOX FOR UNIT 14

Review the unit and decide, were there any points you feel that you should revise or discuss with your tutor?

Do you understand all of the 'Keywords' ?

Use the box below to record your progress :-

KEYWORDS FOR UNIT 14 :-
5% LEVEL OF SIGNIFICANCE, ONE TAILED TESTS, *TWO TAILED TESTS, DEGREES OF FREEDOM,* *TYPE 1 ERROR,   TYPE 2 ERROR.*
Revision Areas :-

....

....

....

....

....

....

....

....

....

UNIT 15 - SELECTION OF STATISTICAL TESTS.

To date, we have examined the varied methods of collecting data. The several forms it may take and the means by which we may decide, whether or not it has significance in the light of our stated hypotheses. In passing, I have mentioned the use of statistical tests and in this section, we shall examine the processes involved in selecting the appropriate test for the data to be analysed.

The selection of the correct test is vitally important. If the wrong test is used, then the analysis produced may well reject an hypothesis which should, had the right test been applied, have been accepted.

When we refer to statistical tests, they are identified as being either :-

PARAMETRIC

or

NON PARAMETRIC.

The term parametric refers, to the nature of the data to be tested. Remember, that data may be in any one of three forms :-

- Continuous (or Interval)

- Rank (or Ordinal)

- Discrete (or Nominal)

Thus, the type of test we choose is (in part) governed by the nature of the data collected.

PARAMETRIC TESTS

Generally speaking, the parametric tests are more powerful and sophisticated and thus the variables analysed within them must meet fairly stringent requirements.
These requirements are that :-

1. The data should be collected (or drawn from) a population which is 'normally distributed'. This means that if a frequency diagram of the population's data was drawn, it should closely resemble a normal distribution curve. In other words, we expect that the data will fall into three bands :-

    - Some high scores

    - Some low scores

    - The bulk of the scores gathered around the mid range or mean.

2. The data collected must be at least of the 'Continuous' (type).

3. The data collected must have an **equal variance.** This is often called 'Homogeneity of variance'. In simple terms this means that the data, from each sampled group should, 'on average', vary (or differ) from their (individual) means by similar amounts.

Although in an ideal world, all of the above criteria would be met, it is often the case that data actually breaks some of these rules. However, this is rarely a problem as the parametric tests are said to be quite 'robust'. i.e. they will stand quite a lot of abuse as a result of inappropriate data being fed into them.

The tests themselves derive much of their power from the way in which they utilise all of the information derivable from the data. They take into account the actual 'size' of the scores, not just the intervals between them, or their named categories as do the less powerful Non Parametric tests. However, as with most things in life, there is a cost to be paid for this increased efficiency. The tests are usually quite complex to calculate and of course, as mentioned, the type of data to which they may be applied is somewhat limited.

NON PARAMETRIC DATA

This data, as the name implies, is data which breaks the above mentioned conditions :-

- The data need not be from a normally distributed population.

- It need not be continuous (or interval) data.

- The sets of data being tested, may swing unequally about the mean.

The non parametric tests are less 'refined', simply because they usually have less informative data fed into them. However, as a bonus, they are usually simpler to calculate.

FURTHER CONSIDERATIONS.

Another consideration when we decide upon the appropriate test to use is the nature of the study itself. Is the design Repeated Measures, or Independent Subjects? Sometimes these are referred to as related, or non related designs.

THE DECISION PROCESS FOR TEST SELECTION.

The first decision to be made is :-

    i.   Are we testing for a difference in the 'mean' performance between two groups ?

  or

    ii.   Are we testing for some relationship or correlation between the two groups' performance ?

If we decide that we are testing for a 'difference', then we must ask, are the variables involved :-

        Continuous, Rank or Discrete ?

Having made this broad distinction, we then work down through the table shown below to arrive at the correct test.

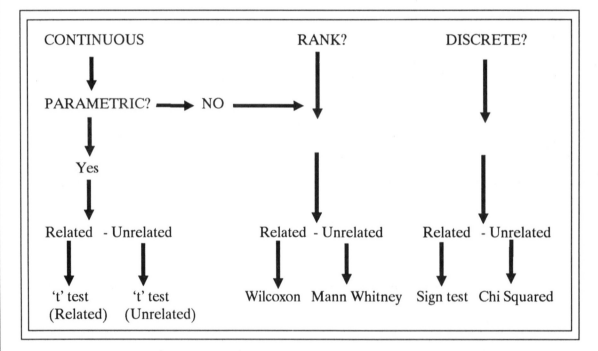

Note ! - This table is reproduced in Appendix A at the rear of the pack. Remove it and use it as a reference.

If we are testing for an 'association, we must still decide :-

Are the variables :-

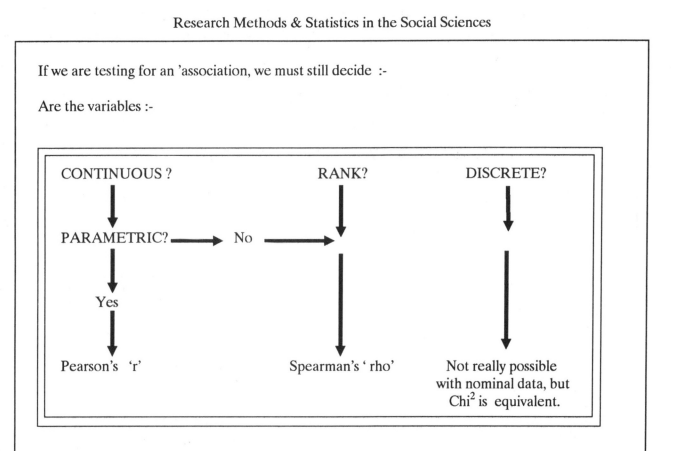

Note ! - This table is also reproduced in Appendix A at the rear of the pack. Remove it and use it as a reference.

Another aid to test selection :-

Below is another table which shows the correct test for various types of data and while the basic decision processes remain the same as that described earlier, it does offer an alternative view.

THE STATISTICAL TESTS

Variables		Test
I.V.	D.V.	
C	C	Spearman's Rho.
D	C	F Test
D	C	Sign Test
D	C (INDEP.)	't' Test
D	C (REP.)	't' Test
R	R	Pearson's r
D	R (INDEP.)	Mann Whitney
D	R (REP.)	Wilcoxon
D	D	Chi Squared

Key :-

I.V.	= Independent Variable
D.V.	= Dependent Variable
C	= Continuous Variable
D	= Discrete Variable
R	= Ranked Variable
INDEP	= Independent Design
REP	= Repeated Design

Note ! - This table is reproduced in an Appendix A, at the rear of the pack. Remove it and use it as a reference.

PROGRESS BOX FOR UNIT 15.

Review the unit and decide, were there any points you feel that you should revise or discuss with your tutor?

Do you understand all of the 'Keywords'?

Use the box below to record your progress :-

KEYWORDS FOR UNIT 15 :-

PARAMETRIC, NON PARAMETRIC, NORMALLY DISTRIBUTED, EQUAL VARIANCE, HOMOGENEITY.

Revision Areas :-

....

....

....

....

....

....

....

....

....

....

UNIT 16 - THE STATISTICAL TESTS

Having now examined the criteria for test selection in the previous unit, we should now turn our attentions to the statistical tests themselves. I would thoroughly recommend Colin Robson's book - "Experiment, Design and Statistics in Psychology" for associated reading. I have shown the appropriate page numbers for each test.

Initially, the tests are broadly divided into those which are parametric and those which are non parametric. A brief description of each of the tests is given below.

THE PARAMETRIC TESTS.

1.   THE 't' TEST (Robson pp. 88 Repeated Measures, pp. 84 Independent Subs. design).

The 't' test, sometimes called Students 't' test appears in two forms. One version for Repeated Measures designs, one for Independent Subjects designs. On a historical point, the name 'students' is really a consequence of the fact that the test was developed whilst its author, or originator was in the employ of a large company. He was, for reasons of disputed ownership, unable to apply his own name to the test and it has since existed under the rather anonymous 'student' label.

The test is designed (in both its related and unrelated form) to test for a significant difference in the mean performance of any two groups.

2.   PEARSON'S PRODUCT MOMENT CORRELATION COEFFICIENT
(Robson pp.156). (referred to as Pearson's 'r')

A test for association or correlation between two sets of data.

THE NON PARAMETRIC TESTS

1.   THE WILCOXON TEST (Robson pp.126).

Performs a similar function to the 't' test (but on non parametric data) and tests for a significant difference in the distribution of groups. Used in repeated measures designs.

2. THE MANN WHITNEY TEST (Robson pp.122).

Function is as the last test, but used for Independent Subjects.

3. SPEARMAN'S 'rho' (Robson pp.66).

A test for association or correlation between data sets. Based upon ranked variables.

4. THE CHI - SQUARED TEST - symbol is X^2 (Robson pp.102).

This test deals with data reduced to its discrete, or nominal form and the test measures frequency of occurrence. The purpose of the test is to establish whether these frequencies of occurrence, are greater or less than would be expected by 'chance' factors alone.

PROGRESS BOX FOR UNIT 16.

Review the unit and decide, were there any points you feel that you should revise or discuss with your tutor?

Use the box below to record your progress :-

NO KEYWORDS FOR UNIT 16 :-

Revision Areas :-

....

....

....

....

....

....

....

....

....

....

UNIT 17 - CORRELATION CALCULATIONS

The tests for association or correlation, described briefly in the preceding unit are described in more detail below. At the end of this unit, a series of exercises will allow some practice at using these tests.

The tests covered are :-

> SPEARMAN'S RHO

> and   PEARSON'S 'r'

SPEARMAN'S RHO

As explained earlier, this is a NON PARAMETRIC test and is used when the data has been recorded in ORDINAL or rank form or, does not meet the requirements for Parametric tests.

This calculation uses the raw scores after they have been arranged into RANK ORDER and produces a figure which tells us the direction of the relationship (positive or negative) and after reference to statistical tables, whether the relationship is statistically SIGNIFICANT.

PEARSON'S r - (pp. 156 - 159)

A PARAMETRIC TEST, used when the data has been recorded on an Interval scale and meets all of the assumptions for Parametric tests i.e. being normally distributed and showing homogeneity of variance.

It uses the raw scores themselves and is rather more laborious to calculate than Spearman's Rho.

Both of the above calculations will produce as a result, a number which may range from -1 through 0 to +1. The nearer the number is to +1 the greater the degree of positive correlation. As it falls toward Zero this indicates no relationship between the two variables. A number approaching -1 suggests a strong negative correlation.

By referring to the tables in the back of Robson (pp. 164) we can decide whether or not the relationship is a chance occurrence or, if statistically significant, the result of our experimental manipulations. This information will then allow us to :-

- Accept or reject the Alternative or Experimental Hypothesis

or

- Accept or reject the Null Hypothesis

SAQ

- If we achieved a result of .89 as a result of applying a test for correlation, what type of correlation would this suggest ?

- Is Pearson's 'r' a parametric or non - parametric test ?

- What 'type' of data would be suitable for analysis by Spearman's Rho?

Unit 17 - Correlation Calculations

```
*******************************************************
*********************************************************
******************** EXERCISE UNIT *********************
*********************************************************
*******************************************************
```

Please complete the following exercise unit and return your worksheet to your subject tutor

CORRELATION EXERCISES :

Example 3

If we wished to investigate the relationship between children playing outdoor games and catching colds as a result, we may gather data as below. Using this data, apply Spearman's Rho and decide if the result is significant :-

Results - Table 1

Child	1	2	3	4	5	6	7	8	9	10	11	12
Games sessions	5	3	7	0	9	9	2	6	3	4	8	10
Colds	2	2	4	5	4	5	4	3	1	1	4	5

Example 4

Twelve children were given reading and maths tests and the data below was collected. From this data calculate Pearson's r and decide if the result is significant :-

Results - Table 2

Child	1	2	3	4	5	6	7	8	9	10	11	12
Maths Score	32	54	68	93	87	24	49	35	97	62	44	73
Reading	17	13	14	10	16	7	6	18	19	13	9	12

PROGRESS BOX FOR UNIT 17.

Review the unit and decide, were there any points you feel that you should revise or discuss with your tutor?

Use the box below to record your progress :-

NO KEYWORDS FOR UNIT 17 :-

Revision Areas :-

....

....

....

....

....

....

....

....

....

....

UNIT 18 - THE 't' TEST

The 't' test may be applied in one of two forms, either :-

- The 't' test - Independent Samples (Robson pp.86)

or

- The 't' test - related (or Correlated) Samples (Robson pp.88)

In Robson's text there are worked examples of both and each is clearly shown in a step by step sequence.

Below are some sets of sample data, one from a related design study and one from an independent design.

Use the Robson book to work your way through the application of a 't' test to each set of data. Refer to the statistical tables shown at the end of the package to assess the significance of your results :-

Example 1.

In an experiment, a psychologist gave a group of Subjects a memory task. The task was performed under two differing conditions. The data obtained was collected in the form of the number of words recalled under each condition and is shown below.

Subject	Condition A	Condition B
1.	6	6
2.	15	10
3.	13	7
4.	14	8
5.	12	8
6.	16	12
7.	14	10
8.	15	10
9.	18	11
10.	17	9
11.	12	8
12.	7	8
13.	15	8

Apply the 't' test for related data to the above results.

The answers to the 'stages' in these tests are shown overleaf.

Answers to example 1.

Results of summary of stages in calculation of 't' test.

$$\overline{X}_A = 13.38$$

$$\overline{X}_B = 8.85$$

$$\sum d = 59 \text{ (Sum of differences)}$$

$$(\sum d)^2 = 3481$$

$$\sum d^2 = 349$$

$$\overline{d} = 4.54 \text{ (Mean of differences)}$$

$$\text{'t'} = 6.289$$

Example 2.

Another experiment carried out by by the same psychologist, used two groups, 12 in one and 13 in the other. The same memory task was used and the data collected is shown below :-

Group A	Group B
12	12
18	9
12	12
10	8
10	10
14	8
14	7
18	13
12	16
8	11
14	15
14	13
	9

Apply the 't' test for unrelated data to the above results.

The answers to the 'stages' of this test are shown overleaf.

Answers to example 2.

Results of summary of 'stages' of 't' Test.

$N \text{ (Group A)} = 12$ $\qquad$ $N \text{ (Group B)} = 13$

$\sum X_A = 156$ $\qquad$ $\sum X_B = 143$

$\overline{X}_A = 13$ $\qquad$ $\overline{X}_B = 11$

$(\sum X_A)^2 = 24336$ $\qquad$ $(\sum X_B)^2 = 20449$

$t = 1.721$

APPENDIX A

TESTING FOR A DIFFERENCE IN MEANS

**********STATISTICAL TEST SELECTION**********

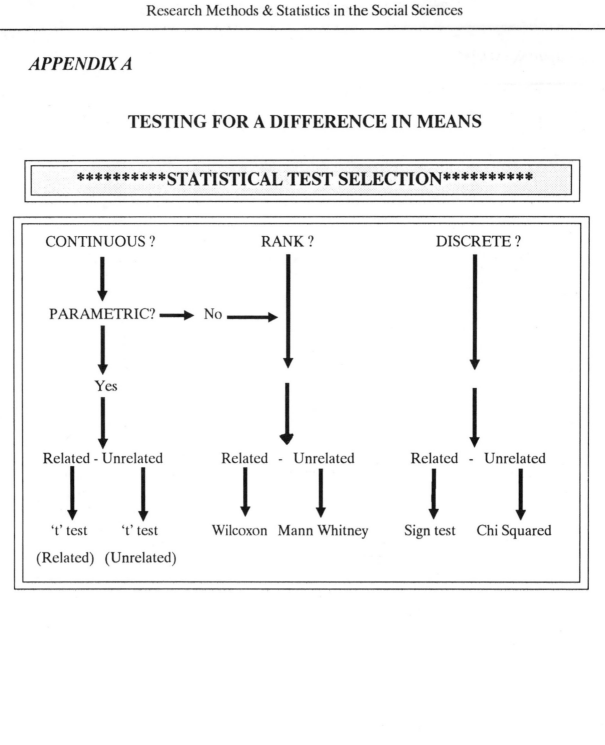

APPENDIX A

TESTING FOR AN ASSOCIATION BETWEEN SETS OF DATA

**********STATISTICAL TEST SELECTION**********

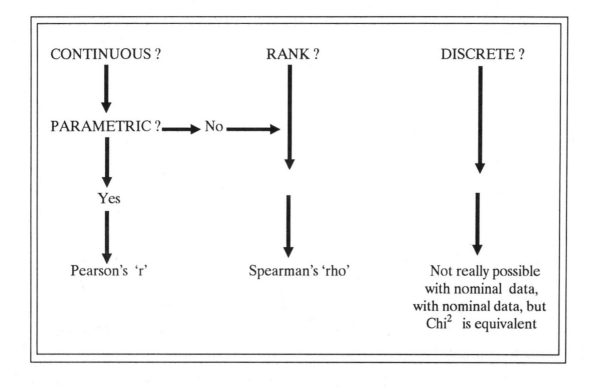

CONTINUOUS ?   RANK ?   DISCRETE ?

PARAMETRIC ? → No →

Yes

Pearson's 'r'   Spearman's 'rho'   Not really possible
with nominal data,
with nominal data, but
Chi^2 is equivalent

APPENDIX A

**********STATISTIC TEST SELECTION**********

VARIABLES		TEST
I.V.	D.V.	
C	C	Spearman's Rho
D	C	F Test
D	C	Sign Test
D	C (INDEP)	't' Test
D	C (REP)	't' Test
R	R	Pearson's 'r'
D	R (INDEP)	Mann Whitney
D	R (REP)	Wilcoxon
D	D	Chi ^{2} Squared

Key:-

I.V. = Independent Variable

D.V. = Dependent Variable

C = Continuous Variable

D = Discrete Variable

R = Ranked Variable

INDEP = Independent Design

REP = Repeated Design

APPENDIX B

STATISTICAL TABLES

Critical Values of Spearman's Rho

		Level of sig. for 2 tailed test			
		0.10	0.05	0.02	0.01
		Level of sig. for 1 tailed test			
		0.05	0.025	0.01	0.005
n=	4	1.000			
	5	0.900	1.000	1.000	
	6	0.829	0.886	0.943	1.000
	7	0.714	0.786	0.893	0.929
	8	0.643	0.738	0.833	0.881
	9	0.600	0.700	0.783	0.833
	10	0.564	0.648	0.745	0.794
	11	0.536	0.618	0.709	0.755
	12	0.503	0.587	0.671	0.727
	13	0.484	0.560	0.648	0.703
	14	0.464	0.538	0.622	0.675
	15	0.443	0.521	0.604	0.654
	16	0.429	0.503	0.582	0.635
	17	0.414	0.486	0.566	0.615
	18	0.401	0.472	0.550	0.600
	19	0.391	0.460	0.535	0.584
	20	0.380	0.447	0.520	0.570
	21	0.370	0.435	0.508	0.566
	22	0.361	0.425	0.496	0.544
	23	0.353	0.415	0.486	0.532
	24	0.344	0.406	0.476	0.521
	25	0.337	0.398	0.466	0.511
	26	0.331	0.390	0.457	0.501
	27	0.324	0.382	0.448	0.491
	28	0.317	0.375	0.440	0.483
	29	0.312	0.368	0.433	0.475
	30	0.306	0.362	0.425	0.467

For n >30 the significance of 'r' can be tested by using the formula :-

$$t = r_s \sqrt{\frac{n-2}{1 - r^2_s}} \qquad df = n - 2$$

and checking the values in table of 't' values.

Calculated value (of 'r') must exceed table value for significance.

APPENDIX B

STATISTICAL TABLES

Critical values of Pearson's 'r'

Level of sig, for 1 tail test.

	0.05	0.025	0.005	0.0005

Level of sig. for 2 tailed test

df = (N - 2)	0.10	0.05	0.01	0.001
2	0.9000	0.9500	0.9900	0.9999
3	0.805	0.878	0.9587	0.9911
4	0.729	0.811	0.9172	0.9741
5	0.669	0.754	0.875	0.9509
6	0.621	0.707	0.834	0.9241
7	0.582	0.666	0.798	0.898
8	0.549	0.632	0.765	0.872
9	0.521	0.602	0.735	0.847
10	0.497	0.576	0.708	0.823
11	0.476	0.553	0.684	0.801
12	0.475	0.532	0.661	0.780
13	0.441	0.514	0.641	0.760
14	0.426	0.497	0.623	0.742
15	0.412	0.482	0.606	0.725
16	0.400	0.468	0.590	0.708
17	0.389	0.456	0.575	0.693
18	0.378	0.444	0.561	0.679
19	0.369	0.433	0.549	0.665
20	0.360	0.423	0.537	0.652
25	0.323	0.381	0.487	0.597
30	0.296	0.349	0.449	0.554
35	0.275	0.325	0.418	0.519
40	0.257	0.304	0.393	0.490
45	0.243	0.288	0.372	0.465
50	0.231	0.273	0.354	0.443
60	0.211	0.250	0.325	0.408
70	0.195	0.232	0.302	0.380
80	0.183	0.217	0.283	0.357
90	0.173	0.205	0.267	0.338
100	0.164	0.195	0.254	0.321

APPENDIX B

STATISTICAL TABLES

Critical Values of 't'

	Level of sig. for 1 tail test			
	0.05	0.025	0.01	0.005
	Level of sig. for 2 tailed test			
Degrees of Freedom	0.10	0.05	0.02	0.01
1	6.314	12.706	31.821	63.657
2	2.920	4.303	6.965	9.925
3	2.353	3.182	4.541	5.841
4.	2.132	2.776	3.747	4.604
5	2.015	2.571	3.365	4.032
6.	1.943	2.447	3.143	3.707
7	1.895	2.365	2.998	3.499
8	1.860	2.306	2.896	3.355
9	1.833	2.262	2.821	3.250
10	1.812	2.228	2.764	3.169
11	1.796	2.201	2.718	3.106
12	1.782	2.179	2.681	3.055
13	1.771	2.160	2.650	3.012
14	1.761	3.145	2.624	2.977
15	1.753	2.131	2.602	2.947
16	1.746	2.120	2.583	2.921
17	1.740	2.110	2.567	2.898
18	1.734	2.101	2.552	2.878
19	1.729	2.093	2.539	2.861
20	1.725	2.086	2.528	2.845
21	1.721	2.080	2.518	2.831
22	1.717	2.074	2.508	2.819
23	1.714	2.069	2.500	2.807
24	1.714	2.064	2.492	2.797
25	1.708	2.060	2.484	2.787
26	1.706	2.056	2.479	2.779
27	1.703	2.052	2.473	2.771
28	1.701	2.048	2.467	2.763
29	1.699	2.045	2.462	2.756
30	1.697	2.042	2.457	2.750
40	1.684	2.021	2.423	2.704
60	1.671	2.000	2.390	2.660
120	1.658	1.980	2.358	2.617
	1.645	1.960	2.326	2.576

Calculated value of 't' must exceed table value for sig.

APPENDIX C

REFERENCES

Broadbent, D.E. (1973)   *In Defence of Empirical Psychology*, Methuen

Heather, N. (1976)   *Perspectives in Psychology,* Methuen

James, W. (1890)   *The Principles of Psychology,* Holt

Milgram, S. (1963)   Behavioural study of obedience. *Journal of Abnormal and Social Psychology,* 67, 371 - 378

Milgram, S. (1965)   *Obedience to Authority,* New York: Harper & Row

Ora, J. P. (1965)   Characteristics of the volunteer for psychological investigations. Office of Naval Research Contract 2149(03), Technical Report 27

Orne, M.T. (1962)   On the social psychology of the psychological experiment: with particular reference to demand characteristics and their implications. *American Psychologist.* 17, 776 - 83.

APPENDIX D

BIBLIOGRAPHY

An Introduction to Experimental Design in Psychology - A Case Approach
H. H. Johnson & R. L. Solso (1978) - Harper & Row (ISBN - 0-06-043413-9)

Experimental Design and Statistics in Psychology - C. Robson (1983) -
Penguin Books (ISBN - 0-14-02.2603-6)

Learning to Use Statistical Tests in Psychology - J. Greene & M'Oliveira (1987) -
Open University Press (ISBN - 0-335-10177-11)

Research Methods - P.McNeill - (1989) Routledge
(ISBN - 0-415-04126-0)

(*Note!*)

The following titles offer a good general coverage of statistics and their 'occasional' misapplication.

How to Lie with Statistics - D. Huff - (1979) - Penguin Books -
(ISBN - 0-14-02.1300-7)

Use and Abuse of Statistics - W.J. Reichman - (1969) - Penguin Books

P 1 5 4 8